D1112683

PENGUIN · SHORT · FICTION

"Not that the story need be long, but it will take a long while to make it short."
— Henry David Thoreau

Dark Arrows
Chronicles of Revenge

Alberto Manguel was born in Buenos Aires, Argentina in 1948. He has lived in France, England, Germany, Italy, Spain and Tahiti and has now made his home in Canada. He is the co-author of *The Dictionary of Imaginary Places*, which has been translated into four languages, and the editor of *Black Water: The Anthology of Fantastic Literature*. Alberto Manguel's book and theatre reviews appear in newspapers and magazines throughout North America. He currently teaches a course in fantastic literature at York University in Toronto.

DARK ARROWS
CHRONICLES OF REVENGE

Collected by

Alberto Manguel

Penguin Books

Penguin Books Canada Ltd., 2801 John Street, Markham, Ontario, Canada L3R 1B4
Penguin Books Ltd., Harmondsworth, Middlesex, England
Penguin Books, 40 West 23rd Street, New York, New York 10010 U.S.A.
Penguin Books Australia Ltd., Ringwood, Victoria, Australia
Penguin Books (N.Z.) Ltd., Private Bag, Takapuna, Auckland 9, New Zealand

First published by Penguin Books Canada Ltd., 1985

Typesetting by Jay Tee Graphics Ltd.
Manufactured in Canada by Gagne Printing Limited

Canadian Cataloguing in Publication Data

Main entry under title:

Dark arrows: chronicles of revenge

(Penguin short fiction)
ISBN 0-14-007712-X

1. Revenge — Fiction. 2. Short Stories.
I. Manguel, Alberto, 1948- . II. Series.

PN6120.2.D37 1985 808.83'1 C85-098535-8

To Elvira Burlando de Meyer,

my grade seven teacher, who confiscated my copy of Ray Bradbury's *Fahrenheit 451* and told me to stop reading rubbish and get down to serious work.

"Avenge now, O Lord of might, noble Giver of glory,
what angers my mind, kindles my heart."

The Anglo-Saxon poem of Judith

"Life being what it is, one dreams of revenge."

Paul Gauguin

Acknowledgements

sher would like to thank the following for permis-
rint copyrighted material:

e of the Round Pond" from *Little Tales of Smethers*
unsany. Reprinted by kind permission of Curtis
. on behalf of John Child Villiers and Valentine
iterary executors of Lord Dunsany. Copyright ©
of the late Lord Dunsany.

y, or the Husband's Revenge" from *Modern*
hort Stories, translated by William L. Grossman
© 1967 The Regents of the University of Califor-
y permission of the University of California Press.

Hunt" from *Collected Stories of William Faulkner.*
by permission of Random House Inc. Copyright ©
newed 1962 by William Faulkner. Also by permis-
rtis Brown Ltd., London. Copyright © William
958.

dling" from *The Marquise of O & Other Stories* by
on Kleist, translated by David Luke and Nigel
nguin Classics 1978), pp. 270–286. Reprinted by
of Penguin Books Ltd. Copyright © David Luke
Reeves 1978.

e No Snakes in Ireland" from *No Comebacks* by
orsyth. Reprinted by permission of Curtis Brown
on. Copyright © Frederick Forsyth 1982.

DARK ARROWS

Conte

Acknowledgements
Introduction
Lord Dunsany
The Pirate of the Round
Bram Stoker
The Squaw
Rachel de Queiroz
Metonymy, or the Husb
William Faulkner
A Bear Hunt
Saki
Sredni Vashtar
Heinrich von Kleist
The Foundling
Frederick Forsyth
There Are No Snakes i
Ken Mitchell
The Great Electrical R
E.L. Doctorow
Willi
Isidoro Blaisten
Uncle Facundo
Rudyard Kipling
Dayspring Mishandle
Edmundo Valadés
Permission for Death
William Trevor
Torridge

The publi
sion to rep

"The Pira
by Lord D
Brown Ltc
Lamb, as
The Estate

"Metonym
Brazilian S
Copyright
nia, used b

"A Bear
Reprinted
1934 and re
sion of Cu
Faulkner 1

"The Four
Heinrich v
Reeves (Pe
permission
and Nigel

"There Ar
Frederick F
Ltd., Lond

''The Great Electrical Revolution'' appeared most recently in *Ken Mitchell Country*, published by Coteau Books. Reprinted by permission of Ken Mitchell. Copyright © Ken Mitchell.

''Willi'' from *Lives of the Poets* by E.L. Doctorow. Reprinted by permission of Random House Inc., and by arrangement with Michael Joseph Ltd., and Pan Books, London. Copyright © 1984 by E.L. Doctorow.

''Uncle Facundo'', translated by Alberto Manguel. Reprinted by permission of Isidoro Blaisten. Copyright © Isidoro Blaisten. English translation Copyright © Alberto Manguel 1985.

''Dayspring Mishandled'' from *Limits and Renewals* by Rudyard Kipling. Reprinted by permission of The National Trust for Places of Historic Interest or Natural Beauty and Macmillan London, Ltd. and Doubleday & Company, Inc. Copyright © 1928 by Rudyard Kipling.

''Permission for Death Is Granted'' by Edmundo Valadés, translated by Alberto Manguel. Reprinted by permission of Fondo de Cultura Economica. Copyright Fondo de Cultura Economica. English translation Copyright © Alberto Manguel 1985.

''Torridge'' from *Lovers of Their Time* by William Trevor. Reprinted by permission of A.D. Peters & Co. Ltd., London and Viking Penguin Inc. Originally published in The New Yorker. Copyright © by William Trevor 1978.

Introduction

Revenge is one of the oldest themes in literature. Flowering in the bosom of God it opens the floodgates of heaven to drown all mankind except an old carpenter and his family; it spurs the Greeks into battle and reduces Troy to ashes; it makes the god of the sea force Ulysses to travel; demanded by the ghost of a Danish king, it drives the melancholy Hamlet to commit murder. Revenge can be grisly but exciting.

As will become apparent in the following collection, there are many different types of revenge, each colouring the act in a different way. There is a common, straightforward revenge where the avenger simply seeks the settlement of a debt. This is the subject of many Westerns: the lone cowboy setting off to find the man who killed his brother, parents, bride, cow, etc. When the debt is paid, the revenge is over.

A superior form of this type of revenge occurs when the driving motive is a desire for what Francis Bacon, the sixteenth-century wise man, called "wild justice." Not only must the debt be paid, a balance must be restored as well: A for B, tit for tat, an eye for an eye. It is not enough for the Count of Monte Cristo to punish those who threw him in jail;

he himself must acquire a certain greatness, become richer and happier than those who were to blame.

Not always is the avenger rewarded: justice is sometimes not only blind, but deaf and dumb as well. Orestes, forced to avenge his father's murder, is pursued by the Furies for what was, after all, a fulfilled obligation. While God (or the gods) demand that justice be done, He seems to reserve that doubtful privilege for Himself. Saint Paul, beseeching the Romans to be charitable and forgive their enemies, asks them not to repay evil with evil because only God has the right to effect revenge. In other words, He will do the dirty work for you. "Vengeance is mine; I will repay, saith the Lord" (Romans 12:19). Paul makes revenge one of the Lord's attributes, like His omnipresence and infinite goodness. Revenge, says Paul, is an act of God.

Whether God's or man's, revenge sometimes hits off target. Bacon describes certain kinds of revenge as "the arrow that flieth in the dark," striking the innocent. In the pile of corpses left on stage at the end of *Hamlet*, not everyone is to blame. On such occasions, justice itself seems more important than those upon whom justice is bestowed.

Finally, revenge can spark off a never-ending story. The white whale tries to kill Captain Ahab who tries to kill the whale; both die in the end, bound by their avenging fate. The true cause is lost in time: neither offender nor offended can remember the reason for their feud. In these cases, revenge stands pure, unsoiled by any explanations.

Whatever the type of revenge, its mechanics suit the mechanics of the story. A does something to B; B responds in a way that will harm A. A has brought on his own downfall, dug his own grave. In the end is the beginning: there is a pleasing tidiness about revenge, a neatness that helps tell a tale.

Of course, once the revenge has taken place, the story ends. The fates of sinner and avenger are rarely, if ever, pursued beyond the final act. As readers, we are seldom interested in the fine sentiments of a lesson learnt; we seldom care about the good manners of morals. Repentance puts an end to conversation; forgiveness becomes the stuff of moralistic tracts. Revenge — bloodthirsty, justice-hungry revenge — is the very essence of romance, lying at the heart of much of the best fiction. From Rudyard Kipling to Heinrich von Kleist, from William Trevor to Rachel de Queiroz, the story of revenge allows the writer to explore the human soul upon the battlefield, its skirmishes, treasons, heroics, shifting sides and alliances and in the end leaving unanswered the question of who is victorious, who is right and who is wrong. There is a pleasing ambiguity in these stories that refuses a conventional conclusion. Maybe the Puritans were not mistaken when they suspected fiction of nourishing the darker side of our heart.

Alberto Manguel
Toronto, February 1985

The Pirate of the Round Pond

Lord Dunsany

Lord Dunsany

(Ireland, 1878-1957)

"Toldees, Monath, Arizim, these are the Inner Lands, the land whose sentinels upon their borders do not behold the sea." With the discovery of these words, Ursula K. LeGuin entered, at the age of twelve, the realm of fantasy that was to make her one of the best writers of the genre today. She read them in an old book found on the living room bookshelf; the author was one Edward John Moreton Drax Plunkett, Lord Dunsany. Like William Blake, Dunsany invented a mythology of terrible and ageless divinities whose tales he then chronicled. His first book was *The Gods of Pegana*, followed by *Time and the Gods*, *The Curse of the Wise Woman* and many others. He had a passion for what he considered aristocratic games: chess, cricket, big-game hunting. He tried his hand (not very successfully) at writing plays and poems. "The Pirate of the Round Pond" is quite unlike anything else Lord Dunsany ever wrote. There are no fantastic creatures here, no supernatural beings, except the mysterious adult looming over a children's world, as large and as menacing as one of the gods of Pegana.

The Pirate of the Round Pond

I've been reading a lot about great men lately; *having* to read about them; Julius Caesar, William the Conqueror, Nelson and Mr Gladstone. But there's a thing I've noticed about grown-ups, and I imagine it applies jolly well to all of them, great and small: they don't keep at it. They may be great just when they're having a battle, or whatever it is, but at other times they'll sit in a chair and read a paper, or talk about the taxes being all wrong, or go out for a walk along a road, when they might be ratting or climbing a tree, or doing anything sensible. Now, Bob Tipling is great the whole time. I should think he is the greatest chap in the world. Anyway he is the greatest chap in our school, by a long way. And he's not only the cleverest, but he's best at cricket and football too. Once he made a hundred runs. And he's a fast bowler too. Well, I can't tell you all about that: there just wouldn't be time. We beat Blikton by an innings and seventy runs, and all because of Bob Tipling. But what I am going to tell you about is about Bob as a pirate, because lots of people have seen him playing cricket, but I and one other boy are the only people in the world besides Bob who know all about him being a pirate. So, if I don't tell about it, probably nobody will, and that would be a pity. Not that I like writing, I'd sooner be out-of-doors. Well, Bob was talking to me once, and I was saying what I'd like to be when I grew up, if I could get the job; and of course that isn't always so easy. What I'd like best of all would be to capture cities, like Alexander and those people; but of course you can't always do that. And then Bob said that he didn't want to be anything when he grew up, because grown-ups were always dull and didn't seem able to enjoy themselves properly, or even to want to: he wanted to be it now. And I asked him what he wanted to be, and he said a pirate. And I asked him what sea he was going to. Now, Bob Tipling always knew all about what he was talking of; more than anybody else; so I can tell you I was pretty surprised when I heard his answer. And yet I knew Bob wasn't talking nonsense. He never does. He said, "The Round Pond." Well, I knew the Round Pond quite well; used to go there most Sundays; but I didn't see how you could be a pirate on the Round Pond. And so I asked Bob. Well, he said he'd had the idea for something like a year, and he'd hung about Kensington Gardens, which was quite near where he lived (both of us for that matter), until he found a boy whose father had lots of money, and he had told the idea to him and he had liked it very much. The idea was to put a pirate ship on the Round Pond, and to fit it out with torpedo tubes.

"How would you do that?" I asked.

"It's already been done," he said. "They're miniature torpedoes, just as it's a miniature ship. There's two of them, one on each side, and we've had a dozen torpedoes made. They are shot out by compressed air, like little air-guns, and there's a good big explosive in them, which goes off when the nose hits anything. They cost a lot to make, but this boy has got lots."

"Does your ship put to sea?" I asked.

"Oh, yes," he said.

"Then how do you fire them?" I said.

"That cost a lot too," he told me. "I touch them off by wireless."

"What will people say," I asked him, "when they see you shooting off your torpedoes from your wireless-set on the bank at their boats?"

"They won't see," said Bob. "But we'll have to be careful about that. We could have it in a large sailing boat at the edge of the water, what they call a parent boat; or we could hide it in a tea basket. Then we wait till a good big ship has put to sea, and we launch the pirate ship so that it should intercept her. If it doesn't we try again and again, until we are lucky. What I want to do is to get the *Rakish Craft* (that is to be her name) head on to her beam at about three or four yards, then we fire a torpedo, and if we meet her somewhere about the middle of the pond, she should never reach land. What do you think of it?"

"I think it's perfectly splendid," I said. "There's only one thing seems to be missing like."

"What's that?" he asked rather sharply.

"Treasure," I said. "Isn't treasure rather the chief part of a pirate's life?"

"That shows all you know about it," he said. "The principal part of a pirate's life is the battles he has, and the thrill of seeing his enemy sink, and the danger, the risk of hanging. I don't say they'd hang me, but I'd go to prison for years if I was caught. And of course if anybody was drowned as a result of the accident, going in to pull out the ship or anything, then I'd be hanged. And even without that, after all I'm a pirate; it doesn't matter where: I might be hanged in any case. Now, I'm giving you a chance you'll probably never have again in a lifetime. Would you like to come in with me?"

Well, of course it was pretty wonderful getting an offer like that from such a tremendous chap as Bob Tipling; because I knew he would be as wonderful as a pirate as he was at everything else. Of course I said, "Yes, rather."

And then he told me what I would have to do. Carry the tea basket chiefly, and walk about and look unconcerned. Or look concerned if he told me to, and walk away from him to draw attention off. "It's full of detectives," he said.

That was on a Saturday morning, and we get the afternoons off on Saturdays. So Bob Tipling told me to meet him at the Round Pond at two o'clock, which I did, and he made me walk up and down looking unconcerned. There were some nice ships there, big sailing ships and some clockwork ones, and even one that went by petrol, a beauty, a big grey ship. "That's the one we'll get if she's there when we put to sea," said Bob. "She'll hole nicely."

And I made the mistake of saying, "Wouldn't it be rather a pity to sink a nice ship like that?"

But Bob explained to me that the people who owned it should think themselves very lucky if their ship was sunk without any loss of life, which wasn't often the case if you were attacked by a pirate. "And, after all, there must be pirates," he said. "And anyhow," he said, "I shall only attack those that deserve it, as Robin Hood used to do on land. The money that that boat cost would have kept a poor man and his family in food for a year. I'm helping the Government, really, to swat the rich. Though that's not the view they'll take if they catch me."

"They ought to," I said.

"We'll just not get caught," said Bob Tipling. "Now walk about concernedly, so that they'll watch you if I want their attention switched off me."

So I did, and it's wonderful how soon I saw one or two men mopping their faces with white handkerchiefs, and making funny little signs. We went away then, because we didn't want people to get to know us.

There were only three of us in it; Bob, me and this rich boy that Bob had found. He had hung about among the trees in Kensington Gardens off and on for nearly a year, before he found this boy walking alone and got a chance to talk to him. He had tried others, of course, but they hadn't enough money. This one had, and he took to the idea at once, as who wouldn't? He had always wanted to be a pirate, and knew that he never would be; and then this chance came to him, brought by Bob. Bob had worked it all out, except the actual making of the torpedoes, and he knew there were people who could make them, and send them off by wireless: all he wanted was the money; and this boy had it, or he could get it out of his father, which comes to the same thing. Bob fixed next Sunday week for putting to sea, under the black and yellow flag with the skull and crossbones; only, Bob said that the actual flag might attract too much attention, and that he would sail under false colours, as pirates often did. We said nothing to each other in school; we almost might have been strangers; but it wouldn't have done to have let a thing like that get out; we should only have been hanged, if it had, before we started. Bob Tipling said that it wasn't a hanging matter. And he would be sure to know. At the same time we were pirates, and I never heard of anything else happening to a pirate, if he got caught, in any book that I've read. So it seemed best not to risk it.

I learned a lot that week in school, but what it was I couldn't tell you, because I was only thinking of one thing all the week, that is of being a pirate. They say it's wicked to be a pirate, and I dare say it is. At the same time nobody could say that it isn't better than sitting indoors at a desk, learning things; especially the kind of things I was learning that week, whatever they were. I never knew a week go by slower. I'd have liked to have timed it, because I should think that it was the slowest week that ever went by. But it came to an end at last, and I slipped away from my home, which is where I lived, and came to the Round Pond at the time Bob Tipling said, which was twelve o'clock on the Sunday morning. I came along the Broad Walk, because I was to meet Bob and his friend there. It was all black earth by the edge of the walk, or dark grey anyway, and there were little trickles of yellow sand in it. I liked the look of the black earth, because it made me think of a wide and desolate moor; and it would have been, if it hadn't been for the grass. And there was a great row of elm trees there, and all the little leaves were just coming out, because it was

Spring. They looked very small and shiny. And at the end of the row I met Bob and his rich friend. Bob had his arms folded and a coloured handkerchief round his neck, and I thought he looked very like a pirate. We were quite near the Round Pond then. Bob introduces me to the rich boy, and his name turns out to be Algernon, and some other name that I forget. And it's just as well to forget it, as we were all involved in piracy together. Bob is away where the police can't catch him now. I'm not going to tell you *my* name. Algernon was carrying a big luncheon basket by a handle, and Bob has the ship on the grass beside him, with a bit of cloth wrapped round it to hide the torpedo tubes.

"That's a nice boat," I says.

"It's a long low rakish craft," said Bob.

Bob was giving the orders, and Algernon and I went down with him to the pond to the part of it where he says, where there was a little kind of a bay. There were lots of ducks on it, mostly black and white ones, and every now and then they would get up out of the water and shake their wings and splash themselves. I suppose they were having a bath. Algernon said they were tufted ducks. And then there was ducks with green heads, that was just ducks. And there was a couple of geese that swam by, honking. And I saw a swan. And there were seagulls, lots of them, flying backwards and forwards over the pond and squawking as they flew. And there were lots of boats. I saw a little sailing boat far out, nearly becalmed, and some clockwork ones like ours. And then all of a sudden I sees the big grey ship that went by petrol. I stopped breathing for a moment when I saw that, and then I pointed her out to Algernon, and Bob nodded his head. And then we both went round to where she was, just beside our little bay, and there was a boy running it that was about the same age as me, which is thirteen. Bob is fourteen, and knows about as much about most things as grown-ups. I don't know about Algernon: I should say he was about the same age as Bob, but nothing near so clever. And just as we came up to where the boy was, a fat little brown spaniel with a wide smile ran up to the boy and licked one of his knees, which was bare. And the boy jumped out of the way. And there was a lady with the brown spaniel, and she said to the boy, "Our Billy won't hurt you." And the boy says, "I am not accustomed to being licked by dogs." "Oh, aren't you?" says Bob.

I don't know if the boy heard him or not.

And then Bob says to me in a lower voice, "That settles the business of it being a pity to sink his nice ship."

There was a fat man standing near, smoking a cigar, evidently the boy's father, and I says to Bob, "Well, it's he that will lose what he paid for the ship if we sink it."

"That's true," said Bob. And he goes up to the fat man with the cigar and says to him, "That's a fine boat your boy's got, sir."

"Yes. You leave it alone," says the fat man.

"Certainly, sir," says Bob.

"Well, that settles it," he says to me. "The ship is doomed."

The big ship touched land just then, and Bob hurried back to his bay, to be ready to launch the *Rakish Craft*, his idea being to launch it just at the right moment to cut off the big grey ship when it sets out again. With the curve that there was on the bay we could send our ship right across her course. I had a very responsible job. I had to unpack the luncheon basket and get my finger on to a knob of the wireless-set that was hidden under some paper packets, and to press it down whenever Bob gave the sign. I can't tell you what the sign was, because I took an oath to Bob that I would never reveal it, but it is something he did with his elbow. Well, the big grey ship set out almost at once. "That's the last she'll see of land," said Bob. But he was wrong there, because our ship didn't quite hit her off, Bob not having had time quite to calculate the speed of the big ship, though he knew the speed of the *Rakish Craft*, and so we were a bit behind her and never fired a torpedo, and we went right across the pond, and the grey ship went very nearly to the other end of it.

Well, the boy ran round and the fat man walked slowly

after him; and, to make a long story short, they puts to sea again. And Bob watches to see about where the grey ship will come in, and goes round and launches the *Rakish Craft* to intercept her about half-way. And Bob said he had calculated the two speeds exactly, but I think it was pure luck. Anyway, the *Rakish Craft*, heading towards Bayswater, comes right up to within nearly two yards of the side of the grey ship, which is sailing towards Hyde Park; and just as the grey ship passes our bows Bob makes the sign with his elbow, and I presses the button where I am sitting on the grass beside the luncheon basket, with my finger inside it touching the wireless-set. And there is a white fountain against the side of the grey ship, and both boats rock a bit, and the big one goes on apparently unconcerned. And I look around, and nobody has noticed a thing. But I couldn't see anything out of the way, myself, except that white splash and the two boats rocking a little, ours more than the other one. For a moment I thought that Bob's game did not work, and then to my delight I saw the big ship's bows dipping a little, or thought I did. Then I saw I was right. She continued straight on her course, but the bows went lower and lower. And all of a sudden her stern went into the air, and she dived right under, and never came up any more. The only thing that could have made it any more perfect would have been a bit of blood on the water. However, one can't have everything. I wanted to cheer, but I caught Bob's eye. Bob strolled round with Algernon to the part of the shore to which our ship was heading, and they hardly glanced at the water. Bob wanted to go on and sink some more boats. But that's where Algernon showed sense, and he told Bob not to do it. That's what they were talking about when on the grass by the luncheon basket. And I joined in with Algernon and said, "Don't do it, Bob. Nobody has suspected a thing, and we can start all fresh next Sunday; but, if you get them suspecting you now, they'll be waiting for you next time you come, and it will probably be prison for all of us."

And Algernon says the same, and between us we just persuaded Bob, and stopped him doing any more piracy that day. But he insisted on hoisting the pirate's flag, the skull and crossbones, yellow on black, because he says you ought to do that as soon as you open fire, whatever colours you have been sailing under till then, and, as he wasn't able to do it at the time, he would do it as soon as he can, and sail across the main once more, as he now called the Round Pond, flying the skull and crossbones. I wasn't easy about it, but nobody seemed to notice, and Bob said it was the right thing to do. I didn't like to look too much at the fat man or his boy, for fear they should catch me looking at them, so I just went on quietly eating a biscuit, and Bob had the sense not to look at them too much either, though his pirate's blood was up. But, as far as I could see when I did take a glance, they were puzzled, and unsuspicious of us. So we packed up the luncheon basket that fired the torpedoes, and Bob put our ship under his arm, and I carried the luncheon basket, and away we walked over the grass, and I never saw three people that looked more innocent-looking. Bob said that we ought to have drunk rum then. And so we would have, if we could have got any. But even Bob's rich friend, Algernon, wasn't able to manage that.

I was pretty-pleased when I went home. I'd always wanted to be a pirate, and now I was one, one of the crew of the *Rakish Craft*, and we'd sunk a big ship. I'm not going to tell you where I lived. Pirates don't do that, if they've got any sense. If there's people looking for one of them they must find out for themselves, without the pirate helping them. I came home to tea; and I wished I could have brought my mother some gold ingots and a few pearls, as pirates often do when they come home. But I remembered what Bob told me, and knew I must think of the glory of it, and not bother about what it ought to be worth in cash. Of course there should have been heaps of gold taken from ships before they were sunk; but it was good enough seeing the grey ship go down, even without any loot. I was only sorry for the seagulls, that they had no corpses floating about. They'd have liked to have pecked at their eyes.

My father and mother wanted to know what I'd been doing, and so did my sister Alice, because they saw that it must have been something. But I couldn't tell them that. And I'm not going to write about my father and mother. They're grown up and can write about themselves if they want to; but I've got my hands full telling about the great battles Bob fought at sea, and the ships that he sunk.

Well, I learned a lot more at school that week. But I can't tell you about that. I've got more important things to write of. Besides, I've forgot it. Bob didn't say a word to me all that week, so that we shouldn't be overheard. And that of course was a good precaution. But he didn't look very precautious. He looked as if his blood was up, and as if he was going on sinking ships till he got hanged, as so many pirates do. I met Bob again at the same place and the same time next Sunday, and he was folding his arms tighter than ever, and wearing that look that I mentioned. I was afraid we would get into trouble. But it was too late to back out now, and, as for warning Bob to go a bit slower, it couldn't be done. I mentioned it to Algernon, but he didn't seem to see it. He'd put his money up, or his father's money, and he wanted to see something for it. So we went to the Round Pond and launched the *Rakish Craft* from one of the little bays. Then I went back on to the grass and got out some sandwiches from the luncheon basket, and watched Bob.

I think Bob was trying for a small sailing boat near the shore, because the *Rakish Craft* just sailed across the little bay, pretty close to the sailing boat, but it didn't come near enough to fire. And when I saw there wasn't going to be a fight, it gave me time to look around. And what did I see when I looked round but that same fat man again and his son, and another fine boat like the last one, even bigger if anything. Well, I saw that before Bob did, because he was watching the sailing boat that he didn't get; and as soon as our *Rakish Craft* came to land again, as she soon did on the other side of the little bay, I moved up nearer to Bob and Algernon, to a bench that there was near the pond, and signed to them to come over, and told them what I had seen. And, just as I thought, as soon as I'd pointed the big ship out, Bob wanted to go and sink it. And I tells him that would be fatal. "Won't they be wondering still what happened to their other boat?" I says to him. "And won't they spend the rest of the day putting two and two together, if they see their new one sink, and see the *Rakish Craft* quite close again and the same crew standing by?"

"Did you ever hear of a pirate sparing anything, when he had it at his mercy?" said Bob.

"Did you ever hear of a pirate that wasn't hanged?" I asks.

"Yes," Bob replies, "all the clever ones."

"And are you being a clever one?" I asks.

And then Algernon joins in, and I admit he showed sense. "Sink smaller craft today," he says, "at the other end of the main from those people, and give them time to forget."

Well, the two of us just succeeded in stopping Bob, and it would have been a bad business if we hadn't. And Bob goes after a smaller ship, as Algernon says, a long way away from the fat man. It was a clockwork ship some way out, and Bob launched the *Rakish Craft* so as to cut it off; and when it gets close he gives me the sign and I presses the button, but he wasn't close enough and it was no good. The torpedo came to the surface then, but it was painted grey so that it wouldn't show up, and very soon it sank, because it only barely floated, and there was a small hole in it so that it would soon fill with water. Nobody noticed it, and the *Rakish Craft* sailed on, under the colours of Spain, which Bob fancied, and came to the other shore, and Bob and Algernon went round and got hold of it, and wound it up and brought it back. And there was the same ship that Bob had missed, putting to sea again, and Bob had a better idea of her pace this time, which was very slow, and he launches the *Rakish Craft* out of the same bay.

It was a lovely day for a fight, and lots of ducks were there enjoying the sun, and the seagulls were flying in flocks over the water. Bob didn't reload the torpedo tube, so as not to attract attention. He still had his starboard torpedo, and he put to sea with that. And this time the *Rakish Craft* headed straight for the enemy. And I wanted to fire, but Bob didn't give the sign until she was quite close, because he had missed the last time. And then he made the sign, and I fired, and both boats rocked a lot when the fountain went up against the side of the enemy's ship, because they were pretty close, and it was a smaller ship than the one we had sunk last time. And then the enemy sailed on a little way, but not far. And soon her bows began to rise out of the water, and very soon after that she slid to the bottom of the sea; and the *Rakish Craft* sailed on to the farther shore. The boy that owned the boat looked quite surprised, but he didn't seem to suspect Bob or Algernon, and of course not me, who was sitting quiet on a bench with the luncheon basket beside me. I watched him so closely that I didn't see what the fat man was doing, or how much he saw.

He was a long way off, but of course you can see anything on the water at almost any distance, and he must have seen the ship sinking if he looked. Bob went round to the far shore with Algernon, and got the *Rakish Craft* when it came in, and hauled down the colours of Spain, which were red and yellow, and hoisted the pirate's flag. I'd sooner he hadn't hoisted the skull and crossbones, but there was no holding Bob over a thing like that. I believed that he had the idea of reloading his two torpedo tubes and putting to sea again and sinking more ships, for I saw that Algernon was arguing with him as they came back. Anyway, he had the sense not to, and Algernon and I got away as quickly as possible. I did a lot of wondering that week. The boy who owned the small ship that we sunk was still there when we left, and he was looking puzzled. I was wondering what he made out about it when he had thought it over. And I was wondering how much the fat man saw, and how much he knew. Well, it wasn't any use wondering. But I couldn't help doing it, for all that. And I was a bit sorry for the boy that had owned the boat, and so I told Bob one day. But Bob said, "Did you ever read of a pirate that was sorry?" And I had to admit that I never had.

"The kites are the only things that I'm sorry for," he said; "not having any dead bodies to peck at."

Of course there weren't any kites; but I saw what he meant; and I saw that it wouldn't be any use to say anything more on those lines to Bob. Well, he gave me my orders where to meet him next Sunday, the same place. Algernon and I were his crew, and of course we had to obey. In a way I was looking forward to that Sunday all the week, because it is a splendid thing to be a pirate and sink ships. But every now and then I couldn't help wondering how far Bob would go, and what would happen to us all if he went too far. And I couldn't ask him. It would have been such cheek.

Well, next Sunday came eventually, and I slipped away as usual and joined Bob and Algernon at the same place. It was a lovely day, and the lilac leaves were all flashing. There would be buds soon. Algernon was there with the luncheon basket as usual, which I took, and we all went down to the pond. And the first thing Bob looks for is ships to sink. But the first thing I looked for was the fat man. And sure enough there he was, with his son and his big ship. And he was nearer to us this time, having come round to our side of the pond. I walked past him, and took a look as I passed, and he looked at me a bit sideways, and I thought he suspected something. But not the boy; he was only watching his big ship. And it was a fine ship, full of funnels and lifeboats and portholes, even better than the one we had sunk. And another thing I noticed; the boy whose ship we had sunk the Sunday before was there again too, and he also had a rather better ship. Who gave it him, I wondered? And I got the idea that the fat man was at the back of it. So I goes back to Bob and tells him that I think the fat man suspects us. And Bob says, "Aren't pirates always suspected?"

And he won't be warned. He has seen the fat man's new ship, and is going to sink her at all costs. I think it's dangerous just then to sink another ship at all, but to sink the fat man's big ship would be absolutely fatal; and so I tell Algernon, and Algernon agrees, and we both of us warn Bob. But Bob says, even if he was going to be hanged for it he would sink that ship first. And when Bob starts talking about the big ship like that, Algernon all of a sudden deserts me and goes in with Bob, and says they will sink her whatever happens. Well, after that I could do nothing, except sit by our wireless set and obey orders. So I sat on the grass, pretending to eat sandwiches, and watching for Bob's sign. And then the big ship came steaming past our bay, close in to the shore and Bob times her exactly, and set sail with the *Rakish Craft*. And it wasn't more than a few minutes before he gave me the sign with both elbows. And I pressed two buttons, and the ships were quite close, and both torpedoes hit. They were so close that our good ship nearly ran into theirs, but just passed astern of her and went on, rocking down to the gunwales. And the other ship went on, after the two fountains had gone up her side, just as the big one did last time, as though nothing had happened. But very soon she begins to dip by the head. And soon after that she takes her last plunge. Well, of course it was perfectly splendid, even if it did mean prison for years: and I looked at the fat man, and his face was half-turned towards me. And somehow there was an expression in it, and I was sure he had found us out. It certainly looked like prison. I packed up the luncheon basket and went over to Bob. "You've done it now," I said. "Let's get away quick, and never come here again."

But you can't stop a pirate when once he has tasted blood. They always go on till they are hanged. "I must hoist my flag," he said, "before I go."

And there was no stopping him. He goes to where his ship comes in to land, and hoists the skull and crossbones and gives the *Rakish Craft* one more run across the bay. And the fat man stands there watching all the time, smoking his cigar, and says nothing. I was glad to see that at least Bob didn't reload his torpedo tubes. And when the *Rakish Craft* reaches shore he takes her out of the water. And the fat man walks up quite close. Bob did have the sense not to run; but we all walked away pretty fast, and got out of Kensington Gardens, never looking behind us once, because we didn't dare. But I knew we were being followed. I don't know how I knew: I just knew. When we got out into Kensington High Street, I said to Bob, "Let's separate, so that they can only follow one of us."

But Bob said that was no good, because if they got one of us that would be all they wanted, to unravel the whole plot. So we kept together and walked over half London, so as to tire out whoever was after us. But that was no good, because the fellow who followed us out of Kensington Gardens made a sign to a nasty-looking fellow ahead of us, who watched us as far as he could see, and then made a sign to another. I knew he was watching us, from the way that he looked so straight in the opposite direction, from the moment we came in sight, the direction in which we were going, so that once we were past him he did not have to trouble to turn his head.

I felt that we never got out of sight of those nasty people. Not even when we separated to go home. What I thought was that they hated everybody, and watched them all, because they thought they were all crooks. I seen them before, and that's what I thought. But we was worse than crooks now. We was pirates. So they were right to watch us. One couldn't deny that. I tried to do a bit of doubling to throw them off, when I got near my home. But it only made it worse.

Well, all Monday and Tuesday I was wondering what was going to happen. And Bob didn't say nothing, either because he didn't believe we had been followed, or because he was pretending that there was nothing wrong. You could never tell with Bob. And Wednesday came, and nothing happened. I still felt uneasy when I went to bed that night; but when I woke up on Thursday morning, and still nothing had happened, I said it was all imagination and nobody had followed us at all, or made little signs at us, silly little signs like lifting their arms and gazing hard at their wrist-watches. But I said as I woke up that Thursday morning that people who lifted their hands up to look at their watches only wanted to see the time, and were meaning no harm to us. So I had a good breakfast and set out to go to school. And there was the fat man walking right past our house, smoking his usual cigar! He was not following me; he was going the other way; but it gave me a feeling like what the man must have had in a poem they taught us at school, which went like this.

As one who walks a lonely road in terror and in dread,
And having once looked round goes on and turns no
more his head,
Because he knows a frightful fiend doth close behind him
tread.

That's how I felt that morning, and all that day; and the next day, and the day after. I knew something was after me. I told Bob that morning that the fat man had found out where I lived.

"Oh, that's nothing," said Bob. "He's got to prove it."

"He's got that boy as a witness," I said, "and probably lots of others."

"Not he," said Bob very airily.

But I don't know how he felt.

"Anyway, I'll never go there again," I said. "So, if by any lucky chance he hasn't got any absolute proof yet, he'll never get any more."

"We'll see about that," said Bob.

And an awful fear came all over me that Bob would make me go back. Because, if we ever went there again, we hadn't a chance. I could see that. And Bob isn't the kind of chap you can disobey, when he says a thing.

Well, the days went on going by, and I was afraid of my own shadow. And they noticed that there was something wrong, at home. But I said it was some work that was worrying me, some lines that I had to learn, and that I couldn't remember. And my father said, "That's right. Keep at it." And my mother said I'd remember them all right. And neither knew the awful thing that was threatening Bob and I. And they tell us at our school that that isn't grammar. But I can tell you I had much too much to think about, that week, to have any time to bother about grammar, even if it was worth bothering about. And of course they didn't know about us being pirates. Well, Saturday came at last, and Bob called me over to him that morning. I think he must have seen something too, for he said, "You may be right about those sleuths.

It may be a coincidence about the fat man passing your house; but I don't believe much in coincidences, and we may be up against it."

"Then you'll never go back to the main," I said, as we all called the Round Pond now.

But Bob was silent. I didn't know what he was going to do, and he wouldn't say.

And that afternoon he said to me, "We're going back to the main."

"We'll all be hanged," I said.

"Oh, no we shan't," said Bob.

"Prison, then," I said, "anyway."

"No," he said. "You may be right about them suspecting us, but what I'm going to do is go back there with my ship, and no torpedo tubes on her. And we'll sail her right across. Then, if they suspect our ship of being a pirate, they'll seize her and see their suspicions are groundless. How can they charge us with sinking ships with torpedoes, when ours is quite unarmed?"

It seemed a good idea, and I felt much better; for I feared that Bob would take me and Algernon to the main and sink another ship, and we'd all go to prison that Sunday.

"And we'll bring the luncheon basket too," says Bob. "And do you know what we'll have in it?"

"No," I says.

"Luncheon," says he.

"That's splendid," I says.

"And then they can bring their charges for damaging property," says Bob; "and see how they'll prove it. Especially when Algernon's father hires a lawyer to prove we are innocent. Piracy indeed! You don't only have to catch your pirate. You have to prove he is one. He is only an alleged pirate till then."

"Yes, we are only alleged pirates," I says, brightening up.

But Bob folds his arms again, and says, "I am a pirate to the last. But still, they'll have to prove it."

That lifted a little of the load off my mind; but I wasn't easy yet, for the fat man knew where I lived, and he must have been very sure of what we had done, to want to track me down like that. And, when Bob went away, most of the old fears came back, and I couldn't look into the future without seeing prison. Well, Bob had fixed the same time on Sunday to meet him near to the main; and so I had to go. And I went, and I met him with Algernon. And the luncheon basket looked lighter. This time, I was glad to see there were no torpedo tubes on the *Rakish Craft*. But he had the pirate's flag flying on her, which seemed a mistake. However, that was Bob's way. And then we went round to the far side of the pond, meaning to sail her right across and take her out and go straight home. That was the north side; and the first thing I sees is the fat man with his boy and his boat, standing on the east side, where he usually is. And he has a big wireless set on the ground beside him, playing a tune to amuse the boy, a tune about teddy bears. Then Bob launches the *Rakish Craft*, with the skull and crossbones flying big and bold from the foremast, and a nice little bit of wind was making it fly. And he winds her up, and off she goes. There was a small sailing ship quite near, and I sees Bob look at it with a wistful look; and I was glad he had no torpedoes, because if he had he'd have sunk her for certain, and we should have all been in gaol; because you can't go on and on doing a thing like that and not get caught. But we've no torpedoes, and nothing in the luncheon basket but luncheon, and the sailing ship goes safe, and the *Rakish Craft* steams on, and the sound of the tune about the teddy bears drifts to us over the water. I see the fat man watching us, and I didn't like it; but I glanced over my shoulder at Bob, and something about the look of him made me see that the more we were watched the better, because the *Rakish Craft* was going about her lawful business that day, and it was a good thing for people to see it. Still, I knew that I wouldn't be easy until she had crossed the main, and we were all on our way home. And then I saw a ship about the same size as ours, putting out from the east shore and coming across. She was faster than ours, and looked like cutting across our course. A pity, I thought for a moment, we hadn't torpedoes. And then I was jolly glad that we had not, because I knew what Bob would have done if his tubes had been loaded.

It was a grey ship, with guns all along her sides; I counted eight of them on each side as she came near, guns that were big enough to have fired a rifle bullet; they seemed rather crowded to me, and I wondered what the ship wanted so many of them for. The ship came on, and the *Rakish Craft* went on, and I thought the other ship would pass right ahead of her. And then it gave a curve and came straight for the *Rakish Craft*. Then I thought it would pass astern of her. And then it gave another twist and came straight for our ship again. Bob and I, and I think Algernon too, realized at the same moment that the manoeuvre was too good to be chance. It must be directed! If wireless could fire torpedoes, it could direct a boat. Even aeroplanes have been directed that way. When the strange ship got quite close, she gave a sudden twist to port, which brought her alongside only a few inches away. It was obvious then that the ship was directed. I looked at Bob, and he had his mouth open. Then I looked across the pond at the fat man, and he was sitting beside his big box that was playing the tune for his boy. But I knew that the tune was only camouflage: the box was much larger than what you'd need, for one thing, to play a tune like that. He was sitting there quite unconcernedly. But the boy wasn't unconcerned: he gave the whole show away, staring at the two ships, glaring would be the right word for it. For a while the two ships kept dead level, quite close; and all of a sudden, bang! And the starboard guns opened fire, the whole broadside. They were pointed downwards, and they hit the *Rakish Craft* just above the waterline on her port side. Several people looked up when they heard the bang. But there was no smoke to speak of, and I don't think anyone spotted where the noise came from, except us, who were watching, and that boy.

I could see the holes in our port side, where every shot had hit; and they must have gone right through and made cracks on our starboard side below the waterline. They wouldn't have been more than cracks, or the *Rakish Craft* would have sunk, but she remained there, rocking on the water. One of the bullets must have gone right into her engines, for she didn't go forward any more. Then the strange ship turned round and sailed back the way she had come, and the *Rakish Craft* stopped rocking. I thought at first that she would keep afloat, and that the breeze, which was proudly flapping her black and yellow flag, would blow her ashore in about ten minutes. But she was making water all the time, and she couldn't last ten minutes. And we saw her go down with her skull and crossbones flying, yellow and black from her mast-head, as a pirate's ship should.

There's not much more to tell, except one funny thing: the fat man launched his grey gunboat again and sent it right across the Round Pond. And she was flying the skull and crossbones too.

The Squaw
Bram Stoker

Bram Stoker

(Ireland, 1847-1912)

The man who wrote *Dracula* was fond of theatre and boxing. Bram Stoker, a tall, sturdy giant with a fiery red beard, became the boxing champion of Dublin University and manager-cum-secretary of the famous Edwardian actor Henry Irving. He had a keen eye for the horrible and was less interested in the niceties of style than in the power of a story. Dracula seems real because he is made of the stuff common to all our nightmares; he is an almost necessary creation, like dragons and unicorns. Bram Stoker's other novels — four of which deal with supernatural: *The Mystery of the Sea, The Jewel of Seven Stars, The Lady of the Shroud,* and *The Lair of the White Worm* — are less successful than *Dracula*. His short fiction, however, is powerfully original, and the collection *Dracula's Guest* contains some of the best horror stories of the turn of the century. Among them is "The Squaw," in which the revenge comes as shock to the reader because it seems impossible that the offended victim could seek justice.

The Squaw

My wife and I, being in the second week of our honeymoon, naturally wanted someone else to join our party, so that when the cheery stranger, Elias P. Hutcheson, hailing from Isthmain City, Bleeding Gulch, Maple Tree County, Neb., turned up at the station at Frankfort, and casually remarked that he was going on to see Nurnberg and that he guessed that so much travelling alone was enough to send an intelligent, active citizen into the melancholy ward of a daft house, we took the pretty broad hint and suggested that we should join forces. We found, on comparing notes afterwards, that we had each intended to speak with some diffidence or hesitation so as not to appear too eager, such not being a good compliment to the success of our married life; but the effect was entirely marred by our both beginning to speak at the same instant — stopping simultaneously and then going on together again. Anyhow, no matter how, it was done; and Elias P. Hutcheson became one of our party. Straightway Amelia and I found the pleasant benefit; instead of quarrelling, as we had been doing, we found that the restraining influence of a third party was such that we now took every opportunity of spooning in odd corners. Amelia declares that ever since she has, as the result of that experience, advised all her friends to take a friend on the honeymoon. Well, we "did" Nurnberg together, and much enjoyed the racy remarks of our Transatlantic friend, who, from his quaint speech and his wonderful stock of adventures, might have stepped out of a novel. We kept for the last object of interest in the city to be visited the Burg, and on the day appointed for the visit strolled round the outer wall of the city by the eastern side.

The Burg is seated on a rock dominating the town, and an immensely deep fosse guards it on the northern side. Nurnberg has been happy in that it was never sacked; had it been it would certainly not be so spick and span perfect as it is at present. The ditch has not been used for centuries, and now its base is spread with tea gardens and orchards, of which some of the trees are of quite respectable growth. As we wandered round the wall, dawdling in the hot July sunshine, we often paused to admire the views spread before us, and in especial the great plain covered with towns and villages and bounded with a blue line of hills, like a landscape of Claude Lorraine. From this we always turned with new delight to the city itself, with its myriad of quaint old gables and acre-wide red roofs dotted with dormer windows, tier upon tier. A little to our right rose the towers of the Burg, and nearer still, standing grim, the Torture Tower, which was, and is, perhaps, the most interesting place in the city. For centuries the tradition of the Iron Virgin of Nurnberg has been handed down as an instance of the horrors of cruelty of which man is capable; we had long looked forward to seeing it; and here at last was its home.

In one of our pauses we leaned over the wall of the moat and looked down. The garden seemed quite fifty or sixty feet below us, and the sun pouring into it with an intense, moveless heat like that of an oven. Beyond rose the grey, grim wall seemingly of endless height, and losing itself right and left in the angles of bastion and counterscarp. Trees and bushes crowned the wall, and above again towered the lofty houses on whose massive beauty Time has only set the hand of approval. The sun was hot and we were lazy; time was our own, and we lingered, leaning on the wall. Just below us was a pretty sight — a great black cat lying stretched in the sun, whilst round her gambolled prettily a tiny black kitten. The mother would wave her tail for the kitten to play with, or would raise her feet and push away the little one as an encouragement to further play. They were just at the foot of the wall, and Elias P. Hutcheson, in order to help the play, stooped and took from the walk a moderate-sized pebble.

"See!" he said, "I will drop it near the kitten, and they will both wonder where it came from."

"Oh, be careful," said my wife; "you might hit the dear little thing!"

"Not me, ma'am," said Elias P. "Why, I'm as tender as a Maine cherry tree. Lor, bless ye, I wouldn't hurt the poor pooty little critter more'n I'd scalp a baby. An' you may bet your variegated socks on that! See, I'll drop it fur away on the outside so's not to go near her!" Thus saying, he leaned over and held his arm out at full length and dropped the stone. It may be that there is some attractive force which draws lesser matters to greater; or more probably that the wall was not plumb but sloped to its base — we not noticing the inclination from above; but the stone fell with a sickening thud that came up to us through the hot air, right on the kitten's head, and shattered out its little brains then and there. The black cat cast a swift upward glance, and we saw her eyes like green fire fixed an instant on Elias P. Hutcheson; and then her attention was given to the kitten, which lay still with just a quiver of her tiny limbs, whilst a thin red stream trickled from a gaping wound. With a muffled cry, such as a human being might give, she bent over the kitten, licking its wound and moaning. Suddenly she seemed to realize that it was dead, and again threw her eyes up at us. I shall never forget this sight, for she looked the perfect incarnation of hate. Her green eyes blazed with lurid fire, and the white, sharp teeth seemed to almost shine through the blood which dabbled her mouth and whiskers. She gnashed her teeth, and her claws stood out stark and at full length on every paw. Then she made a wild rush up the wall as if to reach us, but when the momentum ended fell back, and further added to her horrible appearance for she fell on the kitten, and rose with her back fur smeared with its brains and blood. Amelia turned quite faint, and I had to lift her back from the wall. There was a seat close by in shade of a spreading plane tree, and here I placed her whilst she composed herself. Then I went back to Hutcheson, who stood without moving, looking down on the angry cat below.

As I joined him, he said:

"Wall, I guess that air the savagest beast I ever see — 'cept once when an Apache squaw had an edge on a half-breed what they nicknamed 'Splinters' 'cos of the way he fixed up her papoose which he stole on a raid just to show that he appreciated the way they had given his mother the fire torture. She got that kinder look so set on her face that it just seemed to grow there. She followed Splinters more'n three years till at last the braves got him and handed him over to her. They did say that no man, white or Injun, had ever been so long a-dying under the tortures of the Apaches. The only time I ever see her smile was when I wiped her out. I kem on the camp just in time to see Splinters pass in his checks, and he wasn't sorry to go either. He was a hard citizen, and though I never could shake with him after that papoose business — for it was bitter bad, and he should have been a white man, for he looked like one — I see he had got paid out in full. Durn me, but I took a piece of his hide from one of his skinnin posts an' had it made into a pocketbook. It's here now!" and he slapped the breast pocket of his coat.

Whilst he was speaking, the cat was continuing her frantic efforts to get up the wall. She would take a run back and then charge up, sometimes reaching an incredible height. She did not seem to mind the heavy fall which she got each time but started with renewed vigour; and at every tumble her appearance became more horrible. Hutcheson was a kind-hearted man — my wife and I had both noticed little acts of kindness to animals as well as to persons — and he seemed concerned at the state of fury to which the cat had wrought herself.

''Wall now!'' he said, ''I du declare that that poor critter seems quite desperate. There! there! poor thing, it was all an accident — though that won't bring back your little one to you. Say! I wouldn't have had such a thing happen for a thousand! Just shows what a clumsy fool of a man can do when he tries to play! Seems I'm too darned slipperhanded to even play with a cat. Say Colonel!'' it was a pleasant way he had to bestow titles freely — ''I hope your wife don't hold no grudge against me on account of this unpleasantness? Why, I wouldn't have had it occur on no account.''

He came over to Amelia and apologized profusely, and she with her usual kindness of heart hastened to assure him that she quite understood that it was an accident. Then we all went again to the wall and looked over.

The cat missing Hutcheson's face had drawn back across the moat, and was sitting on her haunches as though ready to spring. Indeed, the very instant she saw him she did spring, and with a blind unreasoning fury, which would have been grotesque, only that it was so frightfully real. She did not try to run up the wall, but simply launched herself at him as though hate and fury could lend her wings to pass straight through the great distance between them. Amelia, womanlike, got quite concerned, and said to Elias P. in a warning voice:

''Oh! You must be very careful. That animal would try to kill you if she were here; her eyes look like positive murder.''

He laughed out jovially. ''Excuse me, ma'am,'' he said, ''but I can't help laughin'. Fancy a man that has fought grizzlies an' Injuns bein' careful of bein' murdered by a cat!''

When the cat heard him laugh, her whole demeanour seemed to change. She no longer tried to jump or run up the wall, but went quietly over, and sitting beside the dead kitten began to lick and fondle it as though it were alive.

"See!" said I, "the effect of a really strong man. Even that animal in the midst of her fury recognizes the voice of a master, and bows to him!"

"Like a squaw!" was the only comment of Elias P. Hutcheson, as we moved over the wall and each time saw the cat following us. At first she had kept going back to the dead kitten, and then as the distance grew greater took it in her mouth and so followed. After a while, however, she abandoned this, for we saw her following all alone; she had evidently hidden the body somewhere. Amelia's alarm grew at the cat's persistence, and more than once she repeated her warning; but the American always laughed with amusement, till finally, seeing that she was beginning to be worried, he said:

"I say, ma'am, you needn't be skeered over that cat. I go heeled, I du!" Here he slapped his pistol pocket at the back of his lumbar region. "Why sooner'n have you worried, I'll shoot the critter, right here, an' risk the police interferin' with a citizen of the United States for carryin' arms contrairy to reg'lations!" As he spoke he looked over the wall, but the cat, on seeing him, retreated, with a growl, into a bed of tall flowers, and was hidden. He went on: "Blest if that ar critter ain't got more sense of what's good for her than most Christians. I guess we've seen the last of her! You bet, she'll go back now to that busted kitten and have a private funeral of it, all to herself!"

Amelia did not like to say more, lest he might, in mistaken kindness to her, fulfil his threat of shooting the cat: and so we went on and crossed the little wooden bridge leading to the gateway whence ran the steep paved roadway between the Burg and the pentagonal Torture Tower. As we crossed the bridge we saw the cat again down below us. When she saw us her fury seemed to return, and she made frantic efforts to get up the steep wall. Hutcheson laughed as he looked down at her, and said:

"Good-bye, old girl. Sorry I in-jured your feelin's, but you'll get over it in time! So long!" And then we passed through the long, dim archway and came to the gate of the Burg.

When we came out again after our survey of this most beautiful old place which not even the well-intended efforts of the Gothic restorers of forty years ago have been able to spoil — though their restoration was then glaring white — we seemed to have quite forgotten the unpleasant episode of the morning. The old lime tree with its great trunk gnarled with the passing of nearly nine centuries, the deep well cut through the heart of the rock by those captives of old, and the lovely view from the city wall whence we heard, spread over almost a full quarter of an hour, the multitudinous chimes of the city, had all helped to wipe out from our minds the incident of the slain kitten.

We were the only visitors who had entered the Torture Tower that morning — so at least said the old custodian — and as we had the place all to ourselves were able to make a minute and more satisfactory survey than would have otherwise been possible. The custodian, looking to us as the sole source of his gains for the day, was willing to meet our wishes in any way. The Torture Tower is truly a grim place, even now when many thousands of visitors have sent a stream of life, and the joy that follows life, into the place; but at the time I mention it wore its primmest and most gruesome aspect. The dust of ages seemed to have settled on it, and the darkness and the horror of its memories seem to have become sentient in a way that would have satisfied the Pantheistic soul of Philo or Spinoza. The lower chamber where we entered was seemingly, in its normal state, filled with incarnate darkness; even the hot sunlight streaming in through the door seemed to be lost in the vast thickness of the walls, and only showed the masonry rough as when the builder's scaffolding had come down, but coated with dust and marked here and there with patches of dark stain which, if walls could speak, could have given their own dread memories of fear and pain. We were glad to pass up the dusty wooden staircase, the custodian leaving the outer door open to light us somewhat on our way; for to our eyes the one long-wick'd, evil-smelling candle stuck in a sconce on the wall gave an inadequate light. When we came up through the open trap in the corner of the chamber overhead, Amelia held on to me so tightly that I could actually feel her heart beat. I must say for my own part that I was not surprised at her fear, for this room was even more gruesome than that below. Here there was certainly more light, but only just sufficient to realize the horrible surroundings of the place. The builders of the tower had evidently intended that only they who should gain the top should have any of the joys of light and prospect. There, as we had noticed from below, were ranges of windows, albeit of mediaeval smallness, but elsewhere in the tower were only a very few narrow slits such as were habitual in places of mediaeval defence. A few of these only lit the chamber, and these so high up in the wall that from no part could the sky be seen through the thickness of the walls. In racks, and leaning in disorder against the walls, were a number of headsmen's swords, great double-handed weapons with broad blade and keen edge. Hard by were several blocks whereon the necks of the victims had lain, with here and there deep notches where the steel had bitten through the guard of flesh and shored into the wood. Round the chamber, placed in all sorts of irregular ways, were many implements of torture which made one's heart ache to see — chairs full of spikes which give instant and excruciating pain; chairs and couches with full knobs whose torture was seemingly less, but which, though slower, were equally efficacious; racks, belts, boots, gloves, collars, all made for compressing at will; steel baskets in which the head could be slowly crushed into a pulp if necessary; watchmen's hooks with long handle and knife that cut at resistance — this a specialty of the old Nurnberg police system; and many, many other devices for man's injury to man. Amelia grew quite pale with horror of the things, but fortunately did not faint, for being a little overcome she sat down on a torture chair, but jumped up again with a shriek, all tendency to faint gone. We both pretended that it was the injury done to her dress by the dust of the chair, and the rusty spikes which had upset her, and Mr Hutcheson acquiesced in accepting the explanation with a kind-hearted laugh.

But the central object in the whole of this chamber of horrors was the engine known as the Iron Virgin, which stood near the centre of the room. It was a rudely-shaped figure of a woman, something of the bell order, or, to make a closer comparison, of the figure of Mrs Noah in the children's Ark, but without that slimness of waist and perfect *rondeur* of hip which marks the aesthetic type of the Noah family. One would hardly have recognized it as intended for a human figure at all had not the founder shaped on the forehead a rude semblance of a woman's face. This machine was coated with rust without, and covered with dust; a rope was fastened to a ring in the front of the figure, about where the waist should have been, and was drawn through a pulley, fastened on the wooden pillar which sustained the flooring above. The custodian pulling this rope showed that a section of the front was hinged like a door at one side; we then saw that the engine was of considerable thickness, leaving just room enough inside for a man to be placed. The door was of equal thickness and of great weight, for it took the custodian all his strength, aided though he was by the contrivance of the pulley, to open it. This weight was partly due to the fact that the door was of manifest purpose hung so as to throw its weight downwards, so that it might shut of its own accord when the strain was released. The inside was honeycombed with rust — nay more, the rust alone that comes through time would hardly have eaten so deep into the iron walls; the rust of the cruel stains was deep indeed! It was only, however, when we came to look at the inside of the door that the diabolical intention was manifest to the full. Here were several long spikes, square and massive, broad at the base and sharp at the points, placed in such a position that when the door should close the upper ones would pierce the eyes of the victim, and the lower ones his heart and vitals. The sight was too much for poor Amelia, and this time she fainted dead off, and I had to carry her down the stairs, and place her on a bench outside till she recovered. That she felt it to the quick was afterwards shown by the fact that my eldest son bears to this day a rude birthmark on his breast, which has, by family consent, been accepted as representing the Nurnberg Virgin.

When we got back to the chamber we found Hutcheson still

opposite the Iron Virgin; he had been evidently philosophizing, and now gave us the benefit of his thought in the shape of a sort of exordium.

"Wall, I guess I've been learnin' somethin' here while madam has been gettin' over her faint. 'Pears to me that we're a long way behind the times on our side of the big drink. We uster think out on the plains that the Injun could give us points in tryin' to make a man oncomfortable; but I guess your old mediaeval law-and-order party could raise him every time. Splinters was pretty good in his bluff on the squaw, but this here young miss held a straight flush all high on him. The points of them spikes air sharp enough still, though even the edges air eaten out by what uster be on them. It'd be a good thing for our Indian section to get some specimens of this here play-toy to send round to the Reservations jest to knock the stuffin' out of the bucks, and the squaws too, by showing them as how old civilization lays over them at their best. Guess but I'll get in that box a minute jest to see how it feels!"

"Oh no! no!" said Amelia. "It is too terrible!"

"Guess, ma'am, nothin's too terrible to the explorin' mind. I've been in some queer places in my time. Spent a night inside a dead horse while a prairie fire swept over me in Montana Territory — an' another time slept inside a dead buffler when the Comanches was on the war path an' I didn't keer to leave my kyard on them. I've been two days in a caved-in tunnel in the Billy Broncho gold mine in New Mexico, an' was one of the four shut up for three parts of a day in the caisson what slid over her side when we was settin' the foundations of the Buffalo Bridge. I've not funked an odd experience yet, an' I don't propose to begin now!"

We saw that he was set on the experiment, so I said: "Well, hurry up, old man, and get through it quick!"

"All right, General," said he, "but I calculate we ain't quite ready yet. The gentlemen, my predecessors, what stood in that thar canister, didn't volunteer for the office — not much! And I guess there was some ornamental tyin' up before the big stroke was made. I want to go into this thing fair and square, so I must get fixed up proper first. I dare say this old galoot can rise some string and tie me up accordin' to sample?''

This was said interrogatively to the old custodian, but the latter, who understood the drift of his speech, though perhaps not appreciating to the full the niceties of dialect and imagery, shook his head. His protest was, however, only formal and made to be overcome. The American thrust a gold piece into his hand, saying, ''Take it, pard; it's your pot; and don't be skeer'd. This ain't no necktie party that you're asked to assist in!'' He produced some thin frayed rope and proceeded to bind our companion, with sufficient strictness for the purpose. When the upper part of his body was bound, Hutcheson said:

''Hold on a moment, Judge. Guess I'm too heavy for you to tote into the canister. You jest let me walk in, and then you can wash up regardin' my legs!''

Whilst speaking he had backed himself into the opening which was just enough to hold him. It was a close fit and no mistake. Amelia looked on with fear in her eyes, but she evidently did not like to say anything. Then the custodian completed his task by tying the American's feet together so that he was now absolutely helpless and fixed in his voluntary prison. He seemed to really enjoy it, and the incipient smile which was habitual to his face blossomed into actuality as he said:

''Guess this here Eve was made out of the rib of a dwarf! There ain't much room for a full-grown citizen of the United States to hustle. We uster make our coffins more roomier in Idaho territory. Now, Judge, you just begin to let this door down, slow, on to me. I want to feel the same pleasure as the other jays had when those spikes began to move toward their eyes!''

''Oh no! no! no!'' broke in Amelia hysterically, ''It is too terrible! I can't bear to see it! — I can't! I can't!''

But the American was obdurate. ''Say, Colonel,'' said he, ''why not take Madame for a little promenade? I wouldn't hurt her feelin's for the world; but now that I am here, havin' kem eight thousand miles, wouldn't it be too hard to give up the very experience I've been pinin' an' pantin' fur? A man can't get to feel like canned goods every time! Me and the Judge here'll fix up this thing in no time, an' then you'll come back, an' we'll laugh together!''

Once more the resolution that is born of curiosity triumphed, and Amelia stayed holding tight to my arm and shivering whilst the custodian began to slacken slowly inch by inch the rope that held back the iron door. Hutcheson's face was positively radiant as his eyes followed the first movements of the spikes.

''Wall!'' he said, ''I guess I've not had enjoyment like this since I left Noo York. Bar a scrap with a French sailor at Wapping — an' that warn't much of a picnic neither — I've not had a show fur real pleasure in this dodrotted Continent, where there ain't no b'ars nor no Injuns, an' wheer nary man goes unheeled. Slow there, Judge! Don't you rush this business! I want a show for my money this game — I du!''

The custodian must have had in him some of the blood of his predecessors in that ghastly tower, for he worked the engine with a deliberate and excruciating slowness which after five minutes, in which the outer edge of the door had not moved half as many inches, began to overcome Amelia. I saw her lips whiten, and felt her hold upon my arm relax. I looked around an instant for a place whereon to lay her, and when I looked at her again found that her eye had become fixed on the side of the Virgin. Following its direction I saw the black cat crouching out of sight. Her green eyes shone like danger lamps in the gloom of the place, and their colour was heightened by the blood which still smeared her coat and reddened her mouth. I cried out:

''The cat! look out for the cat!'' for even then she sprang out before the engine. At this moment she looked like a triumphant demon. Her eyes blazed with ferocity, her hair bristled out till she seemed twice her normal size, and her tail lashed about as does a tiger's when the quarry is before it. Elias P.

Hutcheson when he saw her was amused, and his eyes positively sparkled with fun as he said:

"Darned if the squaw hain't got on all her war paint! Just give her a shove off if she comes any of her tricks on me, for I'm so fixed everlastingly by the boss, that durn my skin if I can keep my eyes from her if she wants them! Easy there, Judge! Don't you slack that ar rope or I'm euchered!"

At this moment Amelia completed her faint, and I had to clutch hold of her round the waist or she would have fallen to the floor. Whilst attending to her I saw the black cat crouching for a spring, and jumped up to turn the creature out.

But at that instant, with a sort of hellish scream, she hurled herself, not as we expected at Hutcheson, but straight at the face of the custodian. Her claws seemed to be tearing wildly as one sees in the Chinese drawings of the dragon rampant, and as I looked I saw one of them light on the poor man's eye, and actually tear through it and down his cheek, leaving a wide band of red where the blood seemed to spurt from every vein.

With a yell of sheer terror which came quicker than even his sense of pain, the man leaped back, dropping as he did so the rope which held back the iron door. I jumped for it, but was too late, for the cord ran like lightning through the pulley-block, and the heavy mass fell forward from its own weight.

As the door closed I caught a glimpse of our poor companion's face. He seemed frozen with terror. His eyes stared with a horrible anguish as if dazed, and no sound came from his lips.

And then the spikes did their work. Happily the end was quick, for when I wrenched open the door they had pierced so deep that they had locked in the bones of the skull through which they had crushed, and actually tore him — it — out of his iron prison till, bound as he was, he fell at full length with a sickly thud upon the floor, the face turning upward as he fell.

I rushed to my wife, lifted her up and carried her out, for I feared for her very reason if she should wake from her faint to such a scene. I laid her on the bench outside and ran back.

Leaning against the wooden column was the custodian moaning in pain whilst he held his reddening handkerchief to his eyes. And sitting on the head of the poor American was the cat, purring loudly as she licked the blood which trickled through the gashed sockets of his eyes.

I think no one will call me cruel because I seized one of the old executioner's swords and shore her in two as she sat.

Metonymy,
or the Husband's Revenge

Rachel de Queiroz

Rachel de Queiroz

(Brazil, b. 1910)

Of the many different literatures of Latin America, that of Brazil is perhaps the one with the strongest individual voice. Its characters, setting and vision of the world seem to owe very little to the major European traditions. Rachel de Queiroz, one of the country's leading novelists, was brought up on her father's plantation in the backlands of Brazil. There she learned about social inequities between the rich and the poor, between men and women. In 1931 she joined the Communist Party, but was expelled two years later when she was accused of Trotskyism. A sense of social outrage permeates de Queiroz's fiction. Her novel *The Three Marias*, one of the first feminist works published in Brazil, chronicles the life of three girls from convent school to womanhood. "Metonymy, or the Husband's Revenge" also reflects the author's social concerns but it is written from within the tradition of absurdist satire established in Brazil at the turn of the century by Machado de Assis and Mario de Andrade.

Metonymy, or the Husband's Revenge

Metonymy. I learned the word in 1930 and shall never forget it. I had just published my first novel. A literary critic had scolded me because my hero went out into the night "chest unclosed."

"What deplorable nonsense!" wrote this eminently sensible gentleman. "Why does she not say what she means? Obviously, it was his shirt unclosed, not his chest."

I accepted the rebuke with humility, indeed with shame. But my illustrious Latin professor, Dr. Matos Peixoto, came to my rescue. He said that what I had written was perfectly correct; that I had used a respectable figure of speech known as metonymy; and that this figure consisted in the use of a word for another word associated with it — for example, a word representing a cause instead of the effect, or representing the container when the content is intended. The classic instance, he told me, is "the sparkling cup"; in reality, not the cup but the wine in it is sparkling.

The professor and I wrote a letter, which was published in the newspaper where the review had appeared. It put my unjust critic in his place. I hope he learned a lesson. I know I did.

Ever since, I have been using metonymy — my only bond with classical rhetoric.

Moreover, I have devoted some thought to it, and I have concluded that metonymy may be more than a figure of speech. There is, I believe, such a thing as practical or applied metonymy. Let me give a crude example, drawn from my own experience. A certain lady of my acquaintance suddenly moved out of the boardinghouse where she had been living for years and became a mortal enemy of the woman who owned it. I asked her why. We both knew that the woman was a kindly soul; she had given my friend injections when she needed them, had often loaned her a hot-water bag, and had always waited on her when she had her little heart attacks. My friend replied:

"It's the telephone in the hall. I hate her for it. Half the time when I answered it, the call was a hoax or joke of some sort."

"But the owner of the boardinghouse didn't perpetrate these hoaxes. She wasn't responsible for them."

"No. But whose telephone was it?"

I know another case of applied metonymy, a more disastrous one for it involved a crime. It happened in a city of the interior, which I shall not name for fear that someone may recognize the parties and revive the scandal. I shall narrate the crime but conceal the criminal.

Well, in this city of the interior there lived a man. He was not old but he was spent, which is worse than being old. In his youth he had suffered from beriberi. His legs were weak, his chest was tired and asthmatic, his skin was yellowish, and his eyes were rheumy. He was, however, a man of property: he owned the house in which he lived and the one next to it, in which he had set up a grocery store. Therefore, although so unattractive personally, he was able to find himself a wife. In all justice to him, he did not tempt fate by marrying a beauty. Instead, he married a poor, emaciated girl, who worked in a men's clothing factory. By her face one would have thought she had consumption. So our friend felt safe. He did not foresee the effects of good nutrition and a healthful life on a woman's appearance. The girl no longer spent eight hours a day at a sewing table. She was the mistress of her house. She ate well: fresh meat, cucumber salad, pork fat with beans and manioc mush, all kinds of sweets, and oranges, which her husband bought by the gross for his customers. The effects were like magic. Her body filled out, especially in the best places. She even seemed to grow taller. And her face — what a change! I may have forgot to mention that her features, in themselves, were good to begin with. Moreover, money enabled her to embellish her natural advantages with art: she began to wear makeup, to wave her hair, and to dress well.

Lovely, attractive, she now found her sickly, prematurely old husband a burden and a bore. Each evening, as soon as the store was closed, he dined, mostly on milk (he could not stomach meat), took his newspaper, and rested on his chaise longue until time to go to bed. He did not care for the movies or for soccer or for radio. He did not even show much interest in love. Just a sort of tepid, tasteless cohabitation.

And then Fate intervened: it produced a sergeant.

Granted, it was unjust for a young wife, after being reconditioned at her husband's expense, to employ her charms to the prejudice of the aforesaid husband. Unjust; but, then, this world thrives on injustice, doesn't it? The sergeant — I shall not say whether he was in the Army, the Air Force, the Marines, or theFusileers, for I still mean to conceal the identities of the parties — the sergeant was muscular, young, ingratiating, with a manly, commanding voice and a healthy spring in his walk. He looked gloriously martial in his high-buttoned uniform.

One day, when the lady was in charge of the counter (while her husband lunched), the sergeant came in. Exactly what happened and what did not happen, is hard to say. It seems that the sergeant asked for a pack of cigarettes. Then he wanted a little vermouth. Finally, he asked permission to listen to the sports broadcast on the radio next to the counter. Maybe it was just an excuse to remain there awhile. In any case, the girl said it would be all right. It is hard to refuse a favor to a sergeant, especially a sergeant like this one. It appears that the sergeant asked nothing more that day. At most, he and the girl exchanged expressive glances and a few agreeable words, murmured so softly that the customers, always alert for something to gossip about, could not hear them.

Three times more the husband lunched while his wife chatted with the sergeant in the store. The flirtation progressed. Then the husband fell ill with a grippe, and the two others went far beyond flirtation. How and when they met, no one was able to discover. The important thing is that they were lovers and that they loved with a forbidden love, like Tristan and Isolde or Paolo and Francesca.

Then Fate, which does not like illicit love and generally punishes those who engage in it, transferred the sergeant to another part of the country.

It is said that only those who love can really know the pain of separation. The girl cried so much that her eyes grew red and swollen. She lost her appetite. Beneath her rouge could be seen the consumptive complexion of earlier times. And these symptoms aroused her husband's suspicion, although, curiously, he had never suspected anything when the love affair was flourishing and everything was wine and roses.

He began to observe her carefully. He scrutinized her in her periods of silence. He listened to her sighs and to the things she murmured in her sleep. He snooped around and found a postcard and book, both with a man's name in the same handwriting. He found the insignia of the sergeant's regiment and concluded that the object of his wife's murmurs, sighs, and silences was not only a man but a soldier. Finally he made the supreme discovery: that they had indeed betrayed him. For he discovered the love letters, bearing airmail stamps, a distant postmark, and the sergeant's name. They left no reasonable doubt.

For five months the poor fellow twisted the poisoned dagger of jealousy in his thin, sickly chest. Like a boy who discovers a birds' nest and, hiding nearby, watches the eggs increasing in number every day, so the husband, using a duplicate key to the wood chest where his wife put her valuables, watched the increase in the number of letters concealed there. He had given her the chest during their honeymoon, saying, "Keep your secrets here." And the ungrateful girl had obeyed him.

Every day at the fateful hour of lunch, she replaced her husband at the counter. But he was not interested in eating. He ran to her room, pulled out a drawer of her bureau, removed the chest from under a lot of panties, slips, and such, took the little key out of his pocket, opened the chest, and anxiously read the new letter. If there was no new letter, he reread the one dated August 21st; it was so full of realism that it sounded like dialogue from a French movie. Then he put everything away and hurried to the kitchen, where he swallowed a few spoonfuls of broth and gnawed at a piece of bread. It was almost impossible to swallow with the passion of those two thieves sticking in his throat.

When the poor man's heart had become utterly saturated with jealousy and hatred, he took a revolver and a box of bullets from the counter drawer; they had been left, years before, by a customer as security for a debt, which had never been paid. He loaded the revolver.

One bright morning at exactly ten o'clock, when the store was full of customers, he excused himself and went through the doorway that connected the store with his home. In a few seconds the customers heard the noise of a row, a woman's scream, and three shots. On the sidewalk in front of the shopkeeper's house they saw his wife on her knees, still screaming, and him, with the revolver in his trembling hand, trying to raise her. The front door of the house was open. Through it, they saw a man's legs, wearing khaki trousers and boots. He was lying face down, with his head and torso in the parlor, not visible from the street.

The husband was the first to speak. Raising his eyes from his wife, he looked at the terror-stricken people and spotted among them his favorite customer. He took a few steps, stood in the doorway, and said:

"You may call the police."

At the police station he explained that he was a deceived husband. The police chief remarked:

"Isn't this a little unusual? Ordinarily you kill your wives. They're weaker than their lovers."

The man was deeply offended.

"No," he protested, "I would be utterly incapable of killing my wife. She is all that I have in the world. She is refined, pretty, and hard-working. She helps me in the store, she understands bookkeeping, she writes the letters to the wholesalers. She is the only person who knows how to prepare my food; I have a special diet. Why should I want to kill my wife?"

"I see," said the chief of police. "So you killed her lover."

The man shook his head.

"Wrong again. The sergeant — her lover — was transferred to a place far away from here. I discovered the affair only after he had gone. By reading his letters. They tell the whole story. I know one of them by heart, the worst of them. . . ."

The police chief did not understand. He said nothing and waited for the husband to continue, which he presently did:

"Those letters! If they were alive I would kill them, one by one. They were shameful to read — almost like a book. I thought of taking an airplane trip. I thought of killing some other sergeant here, so that they would all learn a lesson not to fool around with another man's wife. But I was afraid of the rest of the regiment; you know how these military men stick together. Still, I had to do something. Otherwise I would have gone crazy. I couldn't get those letters out of my head. Even on days when none arrived I felt terrible, worse than my wife. I had to put an end to it, didn't I? So today, at last I did it. I waited till the regular time and, when I saw the wretch appear on the other side of the street, I went into the house, hid behind a door, and lay there for him."

"The lover?" asked the police chief stupidly.

"No, of course not. I told you that I didn't kill her lover. It was those letters. The sergeant sent them — but *he* delivered them. Almost every day, there he was at the door, smiling, with the vile envelope in his hand. I pointed the revolver and fired three times. He didn't say a word; he just fell. No, chief, it wasn't her lover. It was the mailman."

Translated from the Portuguese by William L. Grossman.

A Bear Hunt

William Faulkner

William Faulkner

(United States, 1897-1962)

"The writer's only responsibility is to his art," Faulkner said in an interview in 1956. "He will be completely ruthless if he is a good one. He has a dream. It anguishes him so much he must get rid of it. He has no peace until then. Everything goes by the board: honor, pride, decency, security, happiness, all, to get the book written. If a writer has to rob his mother, he will not hesitate; the 'Ode on a Grecian Urn' is worth any number of old ladies."

Faulkner's first novel, *Soldiers' Pay* (1926), was published by recommendation of his friend Sherwood Anderson, who promised he would back the book if he didn't have to read it. Until the publication of *Sanctuary* in 1931, none of Faulkner's books earned him enough to support himself and his family. His popularity increased somewhat after World War II, and in 1949 he was awarded the Nobel Prize in literature. His influence on Latin American, Italian and French writing has been considerable. Gabriel García Márquez, Cesare Pavese, André Gide have all acknowledged their debt to Faulkner, and in many of their stories the narrator is like Ratliff in "A Bear Hunt," who "may be seen anywhere without surprise." The narrator is commonplace but his story almost impossible, forcing the reader to walk the thin line between belief and disbelief.

A Bear Hunt

Ratliff is telling this. He is a sewing-machine agent; time was when he traveled about our country in a light, strong buckboard drawn by a sturdy, wiry, mismatched team of horses; now he uses a model T Ford, which also carries his demonstrator machine in a tin box on the rear, shaped like a dog kennel and painted to resemble a house.

Ratliff may be seen anywhere without surprise — the only man present at the bazaars and sewing bees of farmers' wives; moving among both men and women at all-day singings at country churches, and singing, too, in a pleasant barytone. He was even at this bear hunt of which he speaks, at the annual hunting camp of Major de Spain in the river bottom twenty miles from town, even though there was no one there to whom he might possibly have sold a machine, since Mrs de Spain doubtless already owned one, unless she had given it to one of her married daughters, and the other man — the man called Lucius Provine — with whom he became involved, to the violent detriment of his face and other members, could not have bought one for his wife even if he would, without Ratliff sold it to him on indefinite credit.

Provine is also a native of the county. But he is forty now and most of his teeth are gone, and it is years now since he and his dead brother and another dead and forgotten contemporary named Jack Bonds were known as the Provine gang and terrorized our quiet town after the unimaginative fashion of wild youth by letting off pistols on the square late Saturday nights or galloping their horses down scurrying and screaming lanes of churchgoing ladies on Sunday morning. Younger citizens of the town do not know him at all save as a tall, apparently strong and healthy man who loafs in a brooding, saturnine fashion wherever he will be allowed, never exactly accepted by any group, and who makes no effort whatever to support his wife and three children.

There are other men among us now whose families are in want; men who, perhaps, would not work anyway, but who now, since the last few years, cannot find work. These all attain and hold to a certain respectability by acting as agents for the manufacturers of minor articles like soap and men's toilet accessories and kitchen objects, being seen constantly about the square and the streets carrying small black sample cases. One day, to our surprise, Provine also appeared with such a case, though within less than a week the town officers discovered that it contained whisky in pint bottles. Major de Spain extricated him somehow, as it was Major de Spain who supported his family by eking out the money which Mrs Provine earned by sewing and such — perhaps as a Roman gesture of salute and farewell to the bright figure which Provine had been before time whipped him.

For there are older men who remember the Butch — he has even lost somewhere in his shabby past the lusty dare-deviltry of the nickname — Provine of twenty years ago; that youth without humor, yet with some driving, inarticulate zest for breathing which has long since burned out of him, who performed in a fine frenzy, which was, perhaps, mostly alcohol, certain outrageous and spontaneous deeds, one of which was the Negro-picnic business. The picnic was at a Negro church a few miles from town. In the midst of it, the two Provines and

Jack Bonds, returning from a dance in the country, rode up with drawn pistols and freshly lit cigars; and taking the Negro men one by one, held the burning cigar ends to the popular celluloid collars of the day, leaving each victim's neck ringed with an abrupt and faint and painless ring of carbon. This is he of whom Ratliff is talking.

But there is one thing more which must be told here in order to set the stage for Ratliff. Five miles farther down the river from Major de Spain's camp, and in an even wilder part of the river's jungle of cane and gum and pin oak, there is an Indian mound. Aboriginal, it rises profoundly and darkly enigmatic, the only elevation of any kind in the wild, flat jungle of river bottom. Even to some of us — children though we were, yet we were descended to literate, town-bred people — it possessed inferences of secret and violent blood, of savage and sudden destruction, as though the yells and hatchets which we associated with Indians through the hidden and secret dime novels which we passed among ourselves were but trivial and momentary manifestations of what dark power still dwelled or lurked there, sinister, a little sardonic, like a dark and nameless beast lightly and lazily slumbering with bloody jaws — this, perhaps, due to the fact that a remnant of a once powerful clan of the Chickasaw tribe still lived beside it under Government protection. They now had American names and they lived as the sparse white people who surrounded them in turn lived.

Yet we never saw them, since they never came to town, having their own settlement and store. When we grew older we realized that they were no wilder or more illiterate than the white people, and that probably their greatest deviation from the norm — and this, in our country, no especial deviation — was the fact that they were a little better than suspect to manufacture moonshine whisky back in the swamps. Yet to us, as children, they were a little fabulous, their swamp-hidden lives inextricable from the life of the dark mound, which some of us had never seen, yet of which we had all heard, as though they had been set by the dark powers to be guardians of it.

As I said, some of us had never seen the mound, yet all of us had heard of it, talked of it as boys will. It was as much a part of our lives and background as the land itself, as the lost Civil War and Sherman's march, or that there were Negroes among us living in economic competition who bore our family names; only more immediate, more potential and alive. When I was fifteen, a companion and I, on a dare, went into the mound one day just at sunset. We saw some of those Indians for the first time; we got directions from them and reached the top of the mound just as the sun set. We had camping equipment with us, but we made no fire. We didn't even make down our beds. We just sat side by side on that mound until it became light enough to find our way back to the road. We didn't talk. When we looked at each other in the gray dawn, our faces were gray, too, quiet, very grave. When we reached town again, we didn't talk either. We just parted and went home and went to bed. That's what we thought, felt, about the mound. We were children, it is true, yet we were descendants of people who read books and who were — or should have been — beyond superstition and impervious to mindless fear.

Now Ratliff tells about Lucius Provine and his hiccup.

When I got back to town, the first fellow I met says, "What happened to your face, Ratliff? Was De Spain using you in place of his bear hounds?"

"No, boys," I says. "Hit was a cattymount."

"What was you trying to do to hit, Ratliff?" a fellow says.

"Boys," I says, "be dog if I know."

And that was the truth. Hit was a good while after they had done hauled Luke Provine offen me that I found that out. Because I never knowed who Old Man Ash was, no more than Luke did. I just knowed that he was Major's nigger, a-helping around camp. All I knowed, when the whole thing started, was what I thought I was aiming to do — to maybe help Luke sho enough, or maybe at the outside to just have a little fun with him without hurting him, or even maybe to do

Major a little favor by getting Luke outen camp for a while. And then hyer hit is about midnight and that durn fellow comes swurging outen the woods wild as a skeered deer, and runs in where they are setting at the poker game, and I says, "Well, you ought to be satisfied. You done run clean out from under them." And he stopped dead still and give me a kind of glare of wild astonishment; he didn't even know that they had quit; and then he swurged all over me like a barn falling down.

Hit sho stopped that poker game. Hit taken three or four of them to drag him offen me, with Major turned in his chair with a set of threes in his hand, a-hammering on the table and hollering cusses. Only a right smart of the helping they done was stepping on my face and hands and feet. Hit was like a fahr — the fellows with the water hose done the most part of the damage.

"What the tarnation hell does this mean?" Major hollers, with three or four fellows holding Luke, and him crying like a baby.

"He set them on me!" Luke says. "He was the one sent me up there, and I'm a-going to kill him!"

"Set who on you?" Major says.

"Them Indians!" Luke says, crying. Then he tried to get at me again, flinging them fellows holding his arms around like they was rag dolls, until Major pure cussed him quiet. He's a man yet. Don't let hit fool you none because he claims he ain't strong enough to work. Maybe hit's because he ain't never wore his strength down toting around one of them little black satchels full of pink galluses and shaving soap. Then Major asked me what hit was all about, and I told him how I had just been trying to help Luke get shed of them hiccups.

Be dog if I didn't feel right sorry for him. I happened to be passing out that way, and so I just thought I would drop in on them and see what luck they was having, and I druv up about sundown, and the first fellow I see was Luke. I wasn't surprised, since this here would be the biggest present gathering of them in the country, let alone the free eating and whisky, so

I says, "Well, this is a surprise." And he says:

"Hic-uh! Hic-ow! Hic-oh! Hic — oh, God!" He had done already had them since nine o'clock the night before; he had been teching the jug ever' time Major offered him one and ever' time he could get to hit when Old Man Ash wasn't looking; and two days before Major had killed a bear, and I reckon Luke had already et more possum-rich bear pork — let alone the venison they had, with maybe a few coons and squirls throwed in for seasoning — than he could have hauled off in a waggin. So here he was, going three times to the minute, like one of these here clock bombs; only hit was bear meat and whisky instead of dynamite, and so he couldn't explode and put himself outen his misery.

They told me how he had done already kept ever'body awake most of the night before, and how Major got up mad anyway, and went off with his gun and Ash to handle them two bear hounds, and Luke following — outen pure misery, I reckon, since he hadn't slept no more than nobody else — walking along behind Major, saying, "Hic-ah! Hic-ow! Hic-oh! Hic — oh, Lord!" until Major turns on him and says:

"Get to hell over yonder with them shotgun fellows on the deer stands. How do you expect me to walk up on a bear or even hear the dogs when they strike? I might as well be riding a motorcycle."

So Luke went on back to where the deer standers was along the log-line levee. I reckon he never so much went away as he kind of died away in the distance like that ere motorcycle Major mentioned. He never tried to be quiet. I reckon he knowed hit wouldn't be no use. He never tried to keep to the open, neither. I reckon he thought that any fool would know from his sound that he wasn't no deer. No. I reckon he was so mizzable by then that he hoped somebody would shoot him. But nobody never, and he come to the first stand, where Uncle Ike McCaslin was, and set down on a log behind Uncle Ike with his elbows on his knees and his face in his hands, going, "Hic-uh! Hic-uh! Hic-uh! Hic-uh!" until Uncle Ike turns and says:

"Confound you, boy; get away from here. Do you reckon any varmint in the world is going to walk up to a hay baler? Go drink some water."

"I done already done that," Luke says, without moving. "I been drinking water since nine o'clock last night. I done already drunk so much water that if I was to fall down I would gush like a artesian well."

"Well, go away anyhow," Uncle Ike says. "Get away from here."

So Luke gets up and kind of staggers away again, kind of dying away like he was run by one of these hyer one-cylinder gasoline engines, only a durn sight more often and regular. He went on down the levee to where the next stand was, and they druv him way from there, and he went on toward the next one. I reckon he was still hoping that somebody would take pity on him and shoot him, because now he kind of seemed to give up. Now, when he come to the "oh, God" part of hit, they said they you could hyear him clean back to camp. They said he would echo back from the canebrake across the river like one of these hyer loud-speakers down in a well. They said that even the dogs on the trail quit baying, and so they all come up and made him come back to camp. That's where he was when I come in. And Old Man Ash was there, too, where him and Major had done come in so Major could take a nap, and neither me nor Luke noticing him except as just another nigger around.

That was hit. Neither one of us knowed or even thought about him. I be dog if hit don't look like sometimes that when a fellow sets out to play a joke, hit ain't another fellow he's playing that joke on; hit's a kind of big power laying still somewhere in the dark that he sets out to prank with without knowing hit, and hit all depends on whether that ere power is in the notion to take a joke or not, whether or not hit blows up right in his face like this one did in mine. Because I says, "You done had them since nine o'clock yesterday? That's nigh twenty-four hours. Seems like to me you'd 'a' done something to try to stop them." And him looking at me like he couldn't make up his mind whether to jump up and bite my head off or just to try to bite hisn off, saying "Hic-uh! Hic-uh!" slow and regular. Then he says,

"I don't want to get shed of them. I like them. But if you had them, I would get shed of them for you. You want to know how?"

"How?" I says.

"I'd just tear your head off. Then you wouldn't have nothing to hiccup with. They wouldn't worry you then. I'd be glad to do hit for you."

"Sho now," I says, looking at him setting there on the kitchen steps — hit was after supper, but he hadn't et none, being as his throat had done turned into a one-way street on him, you might say — going "Hic-uh! Hic-oh! Hic-oh! Hic-uh!" because I reckon Major had done told him what would happen to him if he taken to hollering again. I never meant no harm. Besides, they had done already told me how he had kept everybody awake all night the night before and had done skeered all the game outen that part of the bottom, and besides, the walk might help him to pass his own time. So I says, "I believe I know how you might get shed of them. But, of course, if you don't want to get shed of them —"

And he says, "I just wish somebody would tell me how. I'd pay ten dollars just to set here for one minute without saying 'hic' —" Well, that set him off sho enough. Hit was like up to that time his insides had been satisfied with going "hic-uh" steady, but quiet, but now, when he reminded himself, hit was like he had done opened a cut-out, because right away he begun hollering, "Hic — oh, God!" like when them fellows on the deer stands had made him come back to camp, and I heard Major's feet coming bup-bup-bup across the floor. Even his feet sounded mad, and I says quick,

"Sh-h-h-h! You don't want to get Major mad again, now."

So he quieted some, setting there on the kitchen steps, with Old Man Ash and the other niggers moving around inside the kitchen, and he says, "I will try anything you can sujest. I done tried ever'thing I knowed and ever'thing anybody else told me. I done held my breath and drunk water until I feel just like one of these hyer big automobile tahrs they use to advertise with, and I hung by my knees offen that limb yonder for fifteen minutes and drunk a pint bottle full of water upside down, and somebody said to swallow a buckshot and I done that. And still I got them. What do you know that I can do?''

''Well,'' I says, ''I don't know what you would do. But if hit was me that had them, I'd go up to the mound and get old John Basket to cure me.''

Then he set right still, and then he turned slow and looked at me; I be dog if for a minute he didn't even hiccup. ''John Basket?'' he says.

''Sho,'' I says. ''Them Indians knows all sorts of dodges that white doctors ain't hyeard about yet. He'd be glad to do that much for a white man, too, them pore aboriginees would, because the white folks have been so good to them not only letting them keep that ere hump of dirt that don't nobody want noways, but letting them use names like ourn and selling them flour and sugar and farm tools at not no more than a fair profit above what they would cost a white man. I hyear tell how pretty soon they are even going to start letting them come to town once a week. Old Basket would be glad to cure them hiccups for you.''

''John Basket,'' he says; ''them Indians,'' he says, hiccuping slow and quiet and steady. Then he says right sudden, ''I be dog if I will!'' Then I be dog if hit didn't sound like he was crying. He jumped up and stood there cussing, sounding like he was crying. ''Hit ain't a man hyer has got any mercy on me, white or black. Hyer I done suffered and suffered more than twenty-four hours without food or sleep, and not a sonabitch of them has any mercy or pity on me!''

''Well, I was trying to,'' I says. ''Hit ain't me that's got them. I just thought, seeing as how you had done seemed to got to the place where couldn't no white man help you. But hit ain't no law making you go up there and get shed of them.'' So I made like I was going away. I went back around the corner of the kitchen and watched him set down on the steps again, going ''Hic-uh! Hic-uh!'' slow and quiet again; and then I seen, through the kitchen window, Old Man Ash standing just inside the kitchen door, right still, with his head bent like he was listening. But still I never suspected nothing. Not even did I suspect nothing when, after a while, I watched Luke get up again, sudden but quiet, and stand for a minute looking at the window where the poker game and the folks was, and then look off into the dark towards the road that went down the bottom. Then he went into the house, quiet, and come out a minute later with a lighted lantrun and a shotgun. I don't know whose gun hit was and I don't reckon he did, nor cared neither. He just come out kind of quiet and determined, and went on down the road. I could see the lantrun, but I could hyear him a long time after the lantrun had done disappeared. I had come back around the kitchen then and I was listening to him dying away down the bottom, when old Ash says behind me:

"He gwine up dar?"

"Up where?" I says.

"Up to de mound," he says.

"Why, I be dog if I know," I says. "The last time I talked to him he never sounded like he was fixing to go nowhere. Maybe he just decided to take a walk. Hit might do him some good; make him sleep tonight and help him get up a appetite for breakfast maybe. What do you think?"

But Ash never said nothing. He just went on back into the kitchen. And still I never suspected nothing. How could I? I hadn't never even seen Jefferson in them days. I hadn't never even seen a pair of shoes, let alone two stores in a row or a arc light.

So I went on in where the poker game was, and I says, "Well, gentlemen, I reckon we might get some sleep tonight." And I told them what had happened, because more than like he would stay up there until daylight rather than walk them five miles back in the dark, because maybe them Indians wouldn't mind a little thing like a fellow with hiccups, like white folks would. And I be dog if Major didn't rear up about hit.

"Dammit, Ratliff," he says, "you ought not to done that."

"Why, I just sujested hit to him, Major, for a joke," I says. "I just told him about how old Basket was a kind of doctor. I never expected him to take hit serious. Maybe he ain't even going up there. Maybe's he's just went out after a coon."

But most of them felt about hit like I did. "Let him go," Mr Fraser says. "I hope he walks around all night. Damn if I slept a wink for him all night long . . . . Deal the cards, Uncle Ike."

"Can't stop him now, noways," Uncle Ike says, dealing the cards. "And maybe John Basket can do something for his hiccups. Durn young fool, eating and drinking himself to where he can't talk nor swallow neither. He set behind me on a log this morning, sounding just like a hay baler. I thought once I'd have to shoot him to get rid of him . . . . Queen bets a quarter, gentlemen."

So I set there watching them, thinking now and then about that durn fellow with his shotgun and his lanturn stumbling and blundering along through the woods, walking five miles in the dark to get shed of his hiccups, with the varmints all watching him and wondering just what kind of a hunt this was and just what kind of a two-leg varmint hit was that made a noise like that, and about them Indians up at the mound when he would come walking in, and I would have to laugh until Major says, "What in hell are you mumbling and giggling at?"

"Nothing," I says. "I was just thinking about a fellow I know."

"And damn if you hadn't ought to be out there with him," Major says. Then he decided hit was about drink time and he begun to holler for Ash. Finally I went to the door and hollered for Ash towards the kitchen, but hit was another one of the niggers that answered. When he come in with the demijohn and fixings, Major looks up and says "Where's Ash?"

"He done gone," the nigger says.

"Gone?" Major says. "Gone where?"

"He say he gwine up to'ds de mound," the nigger says. And still I never knowed, never suspected. I just thought to myself, "That old nigger has turned powerful tender-hearted all of a sudden, being skeered for Luke Provine to walk around by himself in the dark. Or maybe Ash likes to listen to them hiccups," I thought to myself.

"Up to the mound?" Major says. "By dad, if he comes back here full of John Basket's bust-skull whisky I'll skin him alive."

"He ain't say what he gwine fer," the nigger says. "All he tell me when he left, he gwine up to'ds de mound and he be back by daylight."

"He better be," Major says. "He better be sober too."

So we set there and they went on playing and me watching them like a durn fool, not suspecting nothing, just thinking how hit was a shame that that durned old nigger would have to come in and spoil Luke's trip, and hit come along towards eleven o'clock and they begun to talk about going to bed, being as they was all going out on stand tomorrow, when we hyeard the sound. Hit sounded like a drove of wild horses coming up that road, and we hadn't no more than turned towards the door, a-asking one another what in tarnation hit could be, with Major just saying, "What in the name of —" when hit come across the porch like a harrycane and down the hall, and the door busted open and there Luke was. He never had no gun and lantrun then, and his clothes was nigh tore clean offen him, and his face looked wild as ere a man in the Jackson a-sylum. But the main thing I noticed was that he wasn't hiccuping now. And this time, too, he was nigh crying.

"They was fixing to kill me!" he says. "They was going to burn me to death! They had done tried me and tied me onto the pile of wood, and one of them was coming with the fahr when I managed to bust loose and run!"

"Who was?" Major says. "What in the tarnation hell are you talking about?"

"Them Indians!" Luke says. "They was fixing to —"

"What?" Major hollers. "Damn to blue blazes, what?"

And that was where I had to put my foot in hit. He hadn't never seen me until then. "At least they cured your hiccups," I says.

Hit was then that he stopped right still. He hadn't never even seen me, but he seen me now. He stopped right still and looked at me with that ere wild face that looked like hit had just escaped from Jackson and had ought to be took back there quick.

"What?" he says.

"Anyway, you done run out from under them hiccups," I says.

Well, sir, he stood there for a full minute. His eyes had done gone blank, and he stood there with his head cocked a little, listening to his own insides. I reckon hit was the first time he had took time to find out that they was gone. He stood there right still for a full minute while that ere kind of shocked astonishment come onto his face. Then he jumped on me. I was still setting in my chair, and I be dog if for a minute I didn't think the roof had done fell in.

Well, they got him offen me at last and got him quieted down, and then they washed me off and give me a drink, and I felt better. But even with that drink I never felt so good but what I felt hit was my duty to my honor to call him outen the back yard, as the fellow says. No, sir. I know when I done made a mistake and guessed wrong; Major de Spain wasn't the only man that caught a bear on that hunt; no, sir. I be dog, if it had been daylight, I'd a hitched up my Ford and taken out of there. But hit was midnight, and besides, that nigger, Ash, was on my mind then. I had just begun to suspect that hit was more to this business than met the nekkid eye. And hit wasn't no good time then to go back to the kitchen then and ask him about hit, because Luke was using the kitchen. Major had give him a drink, too, and he was back there, making up for them two days he hadn't et, talking a right smart about what he aimed to do to such and such a sonabitch that would try to play his durn jokes on him, not mentioning no names; but mostly laying himself in a new set of hiccups, though I ain't going back to see.

So I waited until daylight, until I hyeard the niggers stirring around in the kitchen; then I went back there. And there was old Ash, looking like he always did, oiling Major's boots and setting them behind the stove and then taking up Major's rifle and beginning to load the magazine. He just looked once at my face when I come in, and went on shoving ca'tridges into the gun.

"So you went up to the mound last night," I says. He looked up at me again, quick, and then down again. But he never said nothing, looking like a durned old frizzle-headed ape. "You must know some of them folks up there," I says.

"I knows some of um," he says, shoving ca'tridges into the gun.

"You know old John Basket?" I says.

"I knows some of um," he says, not looking at me.

"Did you see him last night?" I says. He never said nothing at all. So then I changed my tone, like a fellow has to do to get anything outen a nigger. "Look here," I says. "Look at me." He looked at me. "Just what did you do up there last night?"

"Who, me?" he says.

"Come on," I says. "Hit's all over now. Mr Provine has done got over his hiccups and we done both forgot about anything that might have happened when he got back last night. You never went up there just for fun last night. Or maybe hit was something you told them up there, told old man Basket. Was that hit?" He had done quit looking at me, but he never stopped shoving ca'tridges into that gun. He looked quick to both sides. "Come on," I says. "Do you want to tell me what happened up there, or do you want me to mention to Mr Provine that you was mixed up in hit some way?" He never stopped loading the rifle and he never looked at me, but I be dog if I couldn't almost see his mind working. "Come on," I says. "Just what was you doing up there last night?"

Then he told me. I reckon he knowed hit wasn't no use to try to hide hit then; that if I never told Luke, I could still tell Major. "I jest dodged him and got dar first en told um he was a new revenue agent coming up dar tonight, but dat he warn't much en dat all dey had to do was to give um a good skeer en likely he would go away. En dey did en he did."

"Well!" I says. "Well! I always thought I was pretty good at joking folks," I says, "but I take a back seat for you. What happened?" I says. "Did you see hit?"

"Never much happened," he says. "Dey jest went down de road a piece en atter a while hyer he come a-hickin' en a-blumpin' up de road wid de lant'un en de gun. They took de lant'un en de gun away frum him en took him up pon topper de mound en talked de Injun language at him fer a while. Den dey piled up some wood en fixed him on hit so he could git loose in a minute, en den one of dem come up de hill wid de fire, en he done de rest."

"Well!" I says. "Well, I'll be eternally durned!" And then all on a sudden hit struck me. I had done turned and was going out when hit struck me, and I stopped and I says, "There's one more thing I want to know. Why did you do hit?"

Now he set there on the wood box, rubbing the gun with his hand, not looking at me again. "I wuz jest helping you kyo him of dem hiccups."

"Come on," I says. "That wasn't your reason. What was hit? Remember, I got a right smart I can tell Mr Provine and Major both now. I don't know what Major will do, but I know what Mr Provine will do if I was to tell him."

And he set there, rubbing that ere rifle with his hand. He was kind of looking down, like he was thinking. Not like he was trying to decide whether to tell me or not, but like he was remembering something from a long time back. And that's exactly what he was doing, because he says:

"I ain't skeered for him to know. One time dey was a picnic. Hit was a long time back, nigh twenty years ago. He was a young man den, en in de middle of de picnic, him en he brother en nudder white man — I fergit he name — dey rid up wid dey pistols out en cotch us niggers one at a time en burned our collars off. Hit was him dat burnt mine."

"And you waited all this time and went to all this trouble, just to get even with him?" I says.

"Hit warn't dat," he says, rubbing the rifle with his hand. "Hit wuz de collar. Back in dem days a top nigger hand made two dollars a week. I paid fo' bits fer dat collar. Hit wuz blue, wid a red picture of de race betwixt de Natchez en de Robert E. Lee running around hit. He burnt hit up. I makes ten dollars a week now. En I jest wish I knowed where I could buy another collar like dat un fer half of hit. I wish I did."

Sredni Vashtar

Saki

Saki

(Burma, 1870-1916)

In an essay written in 1950, Graham Greene wisely compared the childhood of H.H. Munro — Saki's real name — to that of Kipling. Both were born on the wider shores of the Empire — Kipling in India, Munro in Burma. Both were left by their parents in the care of strangers at a very early age — Kipling with a cruel woman and her weak husband, Munro with two elderly spinsters, Aunt Augusta and Aunt Charlotte. "Unhappiness," says Green, "wonderfully aids the memory, and the best stories of Munro are all of childhood, its humour and its anarchy as well as its cruelty and unhappiness." "Sredni Vashtar" is perhaps the finest example of this.

Saki's sharp-edged stories sparkle with the wit Oscar Wilde put in his dialogue; they are educated, macabre, cynical and wise. In 1914, having established a considerable reputation as a short-story writer, Munro enlisted in the Royal Fusiliers. He died in action in 1916. According to tradition, his last words, cried from a muddy crater near Beaumont Hamel, were: "Put out that bloody cigarette!"

Sredni Vashtar

Conradin was ten years old, and the doctor had pronounced his professional opinion that the boy would not live another five years. The doctor was silky and effete, and counted for little, but his opinion was endorsed by Mrs De Ropp, who counted for nearly everything. Mrs De Ropp was Conradin's cousin and guardian, and in his eyes she represented those three-fifths of the world that are necessary and disagreeable and real; the other two-fifths, in perpetual antagonism to the foregoing, were summed up in himself and his imagination. One of these days Conradin supposed he would succumb to the mastering pressure of wearisome necessary things — such as illnesses and coddling restrictions and drawn-out dullness. Without his imagination, which was rampant under the spur of loneliness, he would have succumbed long ago.

Mrs De Ropp would never, in her honestest moments, have confessed to herself that she disliked Conradin, though she might have been dimly aware that thwarting him "for his good" was a duty which she did not find particularly irksome. Conradin hated her with a desperate sincerity which he was perfectly able to mask. Such few pleasures as he could contrive for himself gained an added relish from the likelihood that they would be displeasing to his guardian, and from the realm of his imagination she was locked out — an unclean thing, which should find no entrance.

In the dull, cheerless garden, overlooked by so many windows that were ready to open with a message not to do this or that, or a reminder that medicines were due, he found little attraction. The few fruit trees that it contained were set jealously apart from his plucking, as though they were rare specimens of their kind blooming in an arid waste; it would probably have been difficult to find a market-gardener who would have offered ten shillings for their entire yearly produce. In a forgotten corner, however, almost hidden behind a dismal shrubbery, was a disused tool shed of respectable proportions, and within its walls Conradin found a haven, something that took on the varying aspects of a playroom and a cathedral. He had peopled it with a legion of familiar phantoms, evoked partly from fragments of history and partly from his own brain, but it also boasted two inmates of flesh and blood. In one corner lived a ragged-plumaged Houdan hen, on which the boy lavished an affection that had scarcely another outlet. Further back in the gloom stood a large hutch, divided into two compartments, one of which was fronted with close iron bars. This was the abode of a large polecat-ferret, which a friendly butcher-boy had once smuggled, cage and all, into its present quarters, in exchange for a long-secreted hoard of small silver. Conradin was dreadfully afraid of the lithe, sharp-fanged beast, but it was his most treasured possession. Its very presence in the tool shed was a secret and fearful joy, to be kept scrupulously from the knowledge of the Woman, as he privately dubbed his cousin. And one day, out of Heaven knows what material, he spun the beast a wonderful name, and from that moment it grew into a god and a religion. The Woman indulged in religion once a week at a church near by, and took Conradin with her, but to him the church service was an alien rite in the House of Rimmon. Every Thursday, in the dim and musty silence of the tool shed, he worshipped with mystic and elaborate ceremonial before the wooden hutch where dwelt Sredni Vashtar, the great ferret. Red flowers in their season and scarlet berries in the wintertime were offered at his shrine, for he was a god who laid some special stress on the fierce impatient side of things, as opposed to the Woman's religion, which, as far as Conradin could observe, went to great lengths in the contrary direction. And on great festivals powdered nutmeg was strewn in front of his hutch, an important feature of the offering being that the nutmeg had to be stolen. These festivals were of irregular occurrence, and were chiefly appointed to celebrate some passing event. On one occasion, when Mrs De Ropp suffered from acute toothache for three days, Conradin kept up the festival during the entire three days, and almost succeeded in persuading himself that Sredni Vashtar was personally responsible for the toothache. If the malady had lasted for another day the supply of nutmeg would have given out.

The Houdan hen was never drawn into the cult of Sredni Vashtar. Conradin had long ago settled that she was an Anabaptist. He did not pretend to have the remotest knowledge as to what an Anabaptist was, but he privately hoped that it was dashing and not very respectable. Mrs De Ropp was the ground plan on which he based and detested all respectability.

After a while Conradin's absorption in the tool shed began to attract the notice of his guardian. "It is not good for him to be pottering down there in all weathers," she promptly decided, and at breakfast one morning she announced that the Houdan hen had been sold and taken away overnight. With her short-sighted eyes she peered at Conradin, waiting for an outbreak of rage and sorrow, which she was ready to rebuke with a flow of excellent precepts and reasoning. But Conradin said nothing: there was nothing to be said. Something perhaps in his white set face gave her a momentary qualm, for at tea that afternoon there was toast on the table, a delicacy which she usually banned on the ground that it was bad for him; also because the making of it "gave trouble," a deadly offence in the middle-class feminine eye.

"I thought you liked toast," she exclaimed, with an injured air, observing that he did not touch it.

"Sometimes," said Conradin.

In the shed that evening there was an innovation in the worship of the hutch-god. Conradin had been wont to chant his praises, tonight he asked a boon.

"Do one thing for me, Sredni Vashtar."

The thing was not specified. As Sredni Vashtar was a god he must be supposed to know. And choking back a sob as he looked at that other empty corner, Conradin went back to the world he so hated.

And every night, in the welcome darkness of his bedroom, and every evening in the dusk of the tool shed, Conradin's bitter litany went up: "Do one thing for me, Sredni Vashtar."

Mrs De Ropp noticed that the visits to the shed did not cease, and one day she made a further journey of inspection.

"What are you keeping in that locked hutch?" she asked. "I believe it's guinea-pigs. I'll have them all cleared away."

Conradin shut his lips tight, but the Woman ransacked his bedroom till she found the carefully hidden key, and forthwith marched down to the shed to complete her discovery. It was a cold afternoon, and Conradin had been bidden to keep to the house. From the furthest window of the dining-room the door of the shed could just be seen beyond the corner of the shrubbery, and there Conradin stationed himself. He saw the Woman enter, and then he imagined her opening the door of the sacred hutch and peering down with her short-sighted eyes into the thick straw bed where his god lay hidden. Perhaps she would prod at the straw in her clumsy impatience. And Conradin fervently breathed his prayer for the last time. But he knew as he prayed that he did not believe. He knew that the Woman would come out presently with that pursed smile he loathed so well on her face, and that in an hour or two the gardener would carry away his wonderful god, a god no longer, but a simple brown ferret in a hutch. And he knew that the Woman would triumph always as she triumphed now, and that he would grow ever more sickly under her pestering and domineering and superior wisdom, till one day nothing would matter much more with him, and the doctor would be proved right. And in the sting and misery of his defeat, he began to chant loudly and defiantly the hymn of his threatened idol:

Sredni Vashtar went forth,
His thoughts were red thoughts and his teeth were white.
His enemies called for peace, but he brought them death.
Sredni Vashtar the Beautiful.

And then of a sudden he stopped his chanting and drew closer to the windowpane. The door of the shed still stood ajar as it had been left, and the minutes were slipping by. They were long minutes, but they slipped by nevertheless. He watched the starlings running and flying in little parties across the lawn; he counted them over and over again, with one eye always on that swinging door. A sour-faced maid came in to lay the table for tea, and still Conradin stood and waited and watched. Hope had crept by inches into his heart, and now a look of triumph began to blaze in his eyes that had only known the wistful patience of defeat. Under his breath, with a furtive exultation, he began once again the paean of victory and devastation. And presently his eyes were rewarded: out through that doorway came a long, low, yellow and brown beast, with eyes a-blink at the waning daylight, and dark wet stains around the fur of jaws and throat. Conradin dropped on his knees. The great polecat-ferret made its way down to a small brook at the foot of the garden, drank for a moment, then crossed a little plank bridge and was lost to sight in the bushes. Such was the passing of Sredni Vashtar.

"Tea is ready," said the sour-faced maid; "where is the mistress?"

"She went down to the shed some time ago," said Conradin.

And while the maid went to summon her mistress to tea, Conradin fished a toasting-fork out of the sideboard drawer and proceeded to toast himself a piece of bread. And during the toasting of it and the buttering of it with much butter and the slow enjoyment of eating it, Conradin listened to the noises and silences which fell in quick spasms beyond the dining room door. The loud foolish screaming of the maid, the answering chorus of wondering ejaculations from the kitchen region, the scuttering footsteps and hurried embassies for outside help, and then, after a lull, the scared sobbings and the shuffling tread of those who bore a heavy burden into the house.

''Whoever will break it to the poor child? I couldn't for the life of me!'' exclaimed a shrill voice. And while they debated the matter among themselves, Conradin made himself another piece of toast.

The Foundling
Heinrich von Kleist

Heinrich von Kleist

(Germany, 1777-1811)

Bernd Heinrich Wilhelm von Kleist was intensely disliked by Goethe, who spoilt the production of Kleist's wonderful comedy, *The Broken Pitcher*, by dividing its single act into three when it was produced in Weimar. Kleist believed that truth was impossible to attain; that all knowledge was illusory, all wisdom deceit. Driven by melancholia, he committed suicide at the age of thirty-four, after shooting his mistress who was suffering from cancer. His dramas, *Prince Friedrich von Homburg* and *Penthesilea*, are less concerned with the sweeping pageantry of classical German drama than with the intimate destinies of individual heroes. His stories were influenced by the *Exemplary Novels* of Cervantes; this is particularly true of stories such as "The Foundling," in which the moral is never apparent, the truth never clear.

The Foundling

Antonio Piachi, a wealthy Roman dealer in property, was sometimes obliged to make long journeys on business. He would then usually leave his young wife Elvira behind in Rome in the care of her relatives. On one of these occasions he travelled with his eleven-year-old son Paolo, the child of an earlier marriage, to Ragusa. It so happened that a plague-like disease had here recently broken out and was spreading panic through the city and the surrounding districts. Piachi, who had not heard this news till he was on his way, stopped on the outskirts to inquire about it. But when he was told that the epidemic was growing daily more serious and that the authorities were talking about closing the town, anxiety on his son's behalf made him abandon all his business plans, and taking horses he set off again the way he had come.

When he was in the open he noticed beside his carriage a young boy who held out his hand towards him beseechingly and appeared to be in great distress. Piachi told the driver to stop, and the boy on being asked what he wanted replied in his innocence that he had caught the plague; that the sheriff's officers were pursuing him to take him to the hospital where his father and mother had already died; and he begged Piachi in the name of all the saints to let him come with him and not leave him behind to perish in the town. As he spoke he clasped the old man's hand, pressed it and kissed it and covered it with tears. Piachi, in his first impulse of horror, was about to push the boy violently away, but the latter at that very moment turned pale and fell fainting to the ground. The good old man's pity was stirred; with his son he got out of his carriage, lifted the boy into it, and drove off, though he had not the least idea what to do with him.

At his first stop he was still negotiating with the people at the inn how he might best get rid of him again when on the orders of the police, who had got wind of the affair, he was arrested; and he and his son and the sick boy, whose name was Nicolo, were transported under guard back to Ragusa. All Piachi's remonstrances against the cruelty of this procedure were in vain; arriving at Ragusa, all three of them were taken in a bailiff's charge to the hospital; and here, although he himself remained well and the boy Nicolo recovered his health, Piachi's son, the eleven-year-old Paolo, became infected and died three days later.

The city gates were now reopened, and Piachi, having buried his son, obtained permission from the police to leave. Grief-stricken, he stepped into his carriage, and at the sight of the now empty seat beside him he took out his handkerchief to weep freely: at that moment Nicolo, cap in hand, stepped up to the carriage and wished him a good journey. Piachi leaned out, and in a voice broken by convulsive sobbing asked the boy whether he would like to travel with him. The latter had no sooner understood the old man than he nodded and answered, "Oh yes, indeed I should!" The hospital authorities, on being asked by the property dealer whether Nicolo might be allowed to accompany him, smiled and assured him that the boy was an orphan and would be missed by nobody. He therefore, greatly moved, lifted him into the carriage and took him back to Rome in place of his son.

On the highway outside the gates Piachi had his first good

look at the boy. He was handsome in a strangely statuesque way; his black hair hung down from his forehead in simple points, overshadowing a serious, wise-looking face which never changed its expression. The old man asked him several questions, but he answered them only briefly; he sat there in the corner, uncommunicative and absorbed in himself, with his hands in his trouser pockets, looking pensively and diffidently out of the windows of the carriage as it sped along. From time to time, with a noiseless movement, he took out a handful of nuts he was carrying with him, and while Piachi wept and wiped his eyes, the boy cracked the shells open between his teeth.

In Rome Piachi introduced him to his excellent young wife Elvira with a brief explanation of what had happened. She could not withhold bitter tears at the thought of her young stepson Paolo, whom she had loved dearly; but she embraced Nicolo, stranger though he was and stiffly as he stood before her, showed him to the bed in which Paolo had slept and gave him all the latter's clothes to wear. Piachi sent him to school where he learnt to read and write and do arithmetic. He had very understandably become all the fonder of the boy for having had to pay so high a price for him; and after only a few weeks, with the consent of the kind-hearted Elvira who had no prospects of bearing her elderly husband any other children, he adopted him as his son. Later, having dismissed from his office a clerk with whom he was for various reasons dissatisfied, he appointed Nicolo in his place, and was delighted with the active and useful assistance which the latter gave him in his complicated business affairs. The only fault that the old man, who was a sworn enemy of all bigotry, had to find with him was the company he kept with the monks of the Carmelite monastery, who were paying very friendly attentions to the boy on account of the large fortune he would one day inherit from his adoptive father; and Elvira's only criticism of Nicolo was that he seemed to have a precocious propensity for the fair sex. For at the age of fifteen he had already, while visiting these monks, succumbed to the wiles of a certain Xaviera

Tartini, a concubine of the bishop's; and although on Piachi's stern insistence he broke off this liaison, Elvira had reason to believe that in these delicate matters Nicolo was not a model of self-denial. When, however, at the age of twenty he married Elvira's niece, Constanza Parquet, an attractive young Genoese lady who had been educated in Rome under her aunt's supervision, this particular trouble at least seemed to have been cured at its source. Both his foster-parents were equally pleased with him, and to give him proof of this they drew up a splendid marriage settlement, making over to him a considerable part of their large and beautiful house. And in short, when Piachi reached the age of sixty he took for Nicolo the final step that a benefactor could take: he gave him legal possession of the entire fortune on which his property business rested, retaining only a small capital for himself, and withdrew with his faithful, virtuous Elvira, whose worldly wishes were few, into retirement.

There was in Elvira's nature an element of silent melancholy, originating in a touching episode that had occurred during her childhood. Her father, Filippo Parquet, was a well-to-do Genoese dyer, and the back of his house, designed for the exercise of his trade, stood right at the sea's edge on a massive stone embankment; huge beams, built into the gable, projected for several yards over the water and were used for hanging out the dyed material. On one ill-fated night fire broke out in the house and at once blazed up in all the rooms simultaneously as if the place were built of pitch and sulphur. The thirteen-year-old Elvira, surrounded on all sides by terrifying flames, fled from staircase to staircase and found herself, she scarcely knew how, standing on one of these beams. The poor child, hanging between heaven and earth, had no idea how to save herself: behind her the fire from the burning gable, fanned by the wind, was already eating into the beam, and beneath her was the wide, desolate, terrible sea. She was just about to commend herself to all the saints, choose the lesser of two evils, and jump down into the water, when suddenly a young Genoese of patrician family appeared in the doorway, threw his cloak over the beam, took her in his arms and with great courage and skill, by clinging to one of the damp cloths that hung down from it, lowered himself into the sea with her. Here they were picked up by the gondolas afloat in the harbour, and carried ashore amid much acclamation from the bystanders. But it turned out that on his way through the house the gallant young man had been severely wounded on the head by a stone falling from the cornice, and it was not long before he lost consciousness and collapsed. He was carried to the house of his father, the marquis, and the latter, when he found that he was taking a long time to recover, summoned doctors from all over Italy who trepanned his son's skull repeatedly and extracted several pieces of bone; but by a mysterious dispensation of Providence all their skill was in vain. Only seldom did he show some signs of life in the presence of Elvira, who had come to nurse him at his mother's request; and after three years of very painful illness, during which the girl did not leave his bedside, he clasped her hand for one last time and expired.

Piachi, who had business connections with this young nobleman's family and made the acquaintance of Elvira in the marquis's house while she was nursing his son, married her two years later; he was particularly careful never to mention the young man's name or otherwise recall him to her, as he knew that her delicate and sensitive mind was deeply disturbed by the memory. The slightest circumstance that even remotely reminded her of the time when this youth had suffered and died for her sake always moved her to tears, and on such occasions there was no comforting or quieting her. She would at once leave whatever company she was in, and no one would follow her, for they knew by experience that the only effective remedy was to let her weep quietly by herself till her grief was stilled. No one except Piachi knew the cause of these strange and frequent fits of emotion, for never in her life had she uttered one word alluding to the episode. They were usually explained as a nervous disorder, the aftermath of a violent fever which she had contracted just after her marriage, and this account served to forestall any further inquiry into their origin.

Nicolo, who despite his father's orders had never wholly severed his connection with the above-mentioned Xaviera Tartini, had on one occasion secretly met her at the carnival without his wife's knowledge, pretending to have been invited to a friend's house; and late that night, when everyone was asleep, he returned home in the costume of a Genoese cavalier which he chanced to have chosen. It so happened that during the night the elderly Piachi felt unwell and Elvira, since the maids were not on hand, had got out of bed to assist him and had gone to fetch a bottle of vinegar from the dining-room. She had just opened the cupboard in the corner and was standing on a chair to search among the glasses and carafes, when Nicolo softly opened the door and stepped into the dining-room in his plumed hat, with cloak and sword, carrying a candle which he had lighted in the hall. Unsuspectingly, without seeing Elvira, he crossed to his bedroom door and had just made the disconcerting discovery that it was locked, when Elvira, standing on her chair behind him with bottles and glasses in her hand, caught sight of him and immediately, as if stricken by some unseen horror, fell to the floor in a dead faint. Nicolo turned round, pale and startled, and was just about to rush to her assistance when he reflected that the noise she had made would certainly bring Piachi to the scene; being anxious to avoid the old man's reproaches at all costs, he snatched with panic haste at a bunch of keys which Elvira carried at her side, and having found one which opened his door he threw the keys back into the dining-room and vanished. Piachi, ill as he was, had jumped out of bed; he lifted up his unhappy wife and rang for the servants, who appeared with lights, and presently Nicolo too came out in his dressing-gown and asked what had happened. But Elvira, her tongue numbed by horror, could not speak, and since Nicolo was the only other person who could have cast any light on the matter, it remained an unexplained mystery. Elvira, trembling in every limb, was carried to her bed, where she lay ill for several days with an acute fever; nevertheless she had enough natural good health to recover tolerably well, and apart from a strange depression with which it left her the incident was without consequence.

A year had thus passed when Constanza, Nicolo's wife, died in childbirth together with her first child. The loss of this virtuous and well-educated young woman was an event not only regrettable in itself but doubly so in that it gave fresh occasion for the indulgence of Nicolo's two vices; his bigotry and his passion for women. Once again he began to linger for days on end in the cells of the Carmelite monks, on the pretext of seeking consolation, although it was known that while his wife was alive he had shown her very little love or fidelity. Indeed, before Constanza had even been buried, Elvira, in the course of making arrangements for the funeral, entered Nicolo's room one evening and found him there with a girl whom, with her painted face and her fripperies, she recognized only too well as Xaviera Tartini's chambermaid. On seeing her, Elvira lowered her eyes and turned and left the room without a word to Nicolo. She said nothing to Piachi or to anyone else about this, and contented herself with kneeling down sadly by Constanza's body and weeping, for the latter had loved Nicolo passionately. But it so happened that Piachi, who had been out in the town, met the girl as he was entering the house; and well realizing what her business here had been, he accosted her sternly and induced her, half by subterfuge and half by force, to give him the letter she was carrying. He went to his room to read it and found that it was, as he had guessed, an urgent message from Nicolo to Xaviera, telling her that he longed for a meeting and asking her to appoint a time and place. Piachi sat down and, disguising his handwriting, replied in Xaviera's name: "Presently, before dark, at the Church of Santa Maria Maddalena." He sealed the note with a borrowed crest and had it handed in to Nicolo's room as if it had just been delivered from the lady. The ruse was entirely successful: Nicolo immediately took his cloak and left the house, without a thought for Constanza who was laid out in her coffin. Thereupon Piachi, in deep indignation, cancelled the solemn funeral which had been arranged for the following day, and summoned a few bearers to take up the laid-out corpse just as it was and carry it quietly, with only himself and Elvira and a few relatives as mourners, to the vault of Santa Maria Maddelena where it was to be buried. Nicolo, waiting wrapped in his cloak at the portico of the church, was astonished by the approach of a funeral procession composed of persons well known to him, and he asked Piachi, who was walking behind the coffin, what this meant and whom they were burying. But the old man, without looking up from the prayer book in his hand, merely answered: "Xaviera Tartini"; whereupon the mourners, entirely ignoring Nicolo's presence, once more uncovered the body and blessed it, and then lowered it into the tomb to be sealed away.

As a result of this deeply humiliating episode, Nicolo was filled with a burning hatred for Elvira, whom he believed to be responsible for the public disgrace which her husband had inflicted on him. For several days Piachi did not speak to him; and since Nicolo nevertheless stood in need of his favour and goodwill in connection with Constanza's estate, he was constrained to seize his adoptive father's hand one evening with every appearance of remorse and swear to give up Xaviera once and for all. He had, however, no intention of keeping this promise; on the contrary, in the face of opposition he merely became more defiant and more cunning in the art of evading the good old man's vigilance. At the same time he thought he had never seen Elvira look more beautiful than at the moment when, to his consternation, she had opened his door and closed it again at the sight of the maid. A soft flush of indignation had lent infinite charm to her gentle face which only seldom showed any emotion; and he thought it incredible that she, with so many attractions, should not herself occasionally walk the primrose path of that indulgence for which she had just punished him so shamefully. He burned with the desire, should this turn out to be the case, to repay her in kind by informing her husband; and all he needed and sought was an opportunity for carrying out this plan.

On one occasion, when Piachi happened to be out of the house, he was passing Elvira's door when he heard, to his surprise, the sound of someone talking in her room. A malicious hope at once flashed through his mind; he stooped down to look and listen through the keyhole and there, great heavens! what should he see but Elvira lying, in an attitude of swooning ecstacy, at someone's feet. He could not make out who it was, but he quite clearly heard her as, in the very accents of passionate love, she whispered the name "Colino." With beating heart he went to the window in the passage and there took up a position from which he could watch her bedroom door without seeming to do so; and presently he heard the latch being quietly raised. Here at last, he told himself, was the exquisite moment for his unmasking of the spurious saint: but instead of the expected stranger it was Elvira herself who emerged from the room, casting a completely unperturbed and indifferent glance at him as she did so. She had a piece of handwoven cloth under her arm, and after locking her room with one of the keys which she carried with her, she walked quite calmly downstairs with her hand on the bannister. To Nicolo this hypocritical display of composure seemed the very height of cynical cunning; she was scarcely out of sight when he rushed to fetch a master key, and after looking cautiously about him he stealthily opened the bedroom door. But to his amazement the room was quite empty, and though he searched every nook and cranny he could find no trace of a man, except for a life-sized portrait of a young cavalier which stood in an alcove behind a red silk curtain, lit by a special lamp. Nicolo was startled, though without knowing why, and as the painted figure stared at him with its wide-open eyes a host of thoughts rushed through his mind. But before he could collect and compose them he began to be apprehensive that Elvira would discover him and punish him in some way; he closed the bedroom door again in some confusion and withdrew.

The more he thought about this remarkable incident, the more convinced he became of the importance of the picture he had discovered, and the more acute and urgent grew his curiosity to know whose portrait it was. For he had clearly seen Elvira's posture: she had been kneeling, and it was quite certain that she had been doing so in front of the young nobleman on the canvas. In the uneasiness of mind that possessed him he went to Xaviera Tartini and told her of his strange experience. Xaviera was just as anxious as Nicolo to discredit Elvira, whom she blamed for all the difficulties that were being put in the way of their liaison; and she declared that she would like to see the portrait in the bedroom. For she could boast an extensive acquaintance among the Italian nobility, and if the young man in question had at any time been in Rome and was a person of the least consequence, the chances were that she would know him. Sure enough it happened before long that Piachi and his wife went into the country one Sunday to visit a relative; and no sooner was the coast thus clear than Nicolo hastened to Xaviera, brought her to the house accompanied by a small daughter whom she had had by the Cardinal, and introduced her into Elvira's room on the pretext that she was a lady wishing to see the paintings and embroideries. But no sooner had he drawn back the curtain than the child, whose name was Clara, utterly confounded him by exclaiming: "Why, God bless us, Signor Nicolo! but that's a picture of you!" Xaviera fell silent. The portrait did indeed, the longer she looked at it, bear a singular resemblance to him, especially when she remembered, as well she might, the Genoese costume he had worn a few months ago for their clandestine visit to the carnival. Nicolo tried to laugh off the sudden flush of embarrassment which came over him; he kissed the little girl and said: "Indeed, my dear Clara, it's about as much like me as you are like the man who thinks he is your father!" But Xaviera, in whom the bitter pangs of jealousy were stirring, merely looked at him; and after stepping in front of the mirror and remarking that after all the identity of the person was a matter of indifference, she took her leave of him rather coldly and left the room.

As soon as Xaviera had gone, Nicolo fell into a great state of excitement over this scene. He remembered with delight the strange and violent turmoil into which Elvira had been thrown by his fanciful appearance on the night of the carnival; and the thought of having inspired a passion in this walking model of womanly virtue was almost as sweet to him as that of taking his revenge on her. Having now the prospect of gratifying both desires at one and the same time, he waited impatiently for Elvira's return and for the moment when he would look into her eyes and crown his still hesitant hopes with certainty. In this elation the one thing that gave him pause was the distinct recollection that when he had spied on her through the keyhole, the name which the kneeling Elvira had addressed to the picture had been "Colino." And yet there was something about the sound of this name — a rather unusual one in Italy — that filled him with sweet reveries, though he could not tell why; and faced with the choice of disbelieving one of two senses, his eyes or his ears, he naturally inclined to the evidence that was more flattering to his desires.

Meanwhile several days passed before Elvira returned from the country, where she had been staying with a cousin; from his house she brought back with her a young kinswoman who wanted to see Rome, and being occupied with polite attentions to this young lady, she cast only a fleeting and insignificant glance at Nicolo as with the most amiable courtesy he helped her out of her carriage. For several weeks, which were devoted to the entertainment of her guest, the house was in an unwonted turmoil; visits were made to places in and outside the city which would be likely to appeal to a young and lively girl; and Nicolo, busy in his office and therefore not invited on any of these expeditions, began again to harbour keen resentment against Elvira. Bitter feelings rankled in him as he thought of the unknown man she so devoutly adored in secret; and the torment of his depraved heart reached its height on the evening after the young kinswoman's departure, an evening for which he had waited with longing, but on which Elvira, instead of speaking to him, sat in silence for an hour at the dining-room table, busy with a piece of needlework. It so happened that Piachi, a few days earlier, had been inquiring after the whereabouts of a box of little ivory letters with which Nicolo had been taught to read as a boy; for since no one needed them now, it had occurred to him to make a present of them to a small child in the neighbourhood. But the maidservant who had been told to look for them among various other discarded objects had only been able to find the six letters that formed the name Nicolo; no doubt because the others, having less relevance to the boy himself, had attracted his interest less, and had at one time or another been thrown away. These six letters had now been lying in the dining-room for several days, and Nicolo, as he sat gloomily brooding at the table with his head propped on his arm, picked them up and toyed with them; and as he did so he discovered — purely by chance for he had never in his life been so astonished — the combination of the letters that spelt the name "Colino." Nicolo, who had been quite unaware of this anagrammatic aspect of his name, was once again seized by the wildest hopes, and cast a hesitant anxious glance at Elvira who was sitting beside him. The correspondence between the two words struck him as more than merely fortuitous; with secret delight he pondered the implications of his strange discovery, and taking his hands from the table he waited with beating heart for the moment when Elvira would look up and see the name lying there plainly visible. His expectations were not disappointed; for no sooner had she, in an idle moment, noticed this display of the letters and unsuspectingly leaned forward (for she was a little short-sighted) to read them, than she fixed a sudden strange look of anguish on Nicolo's face as he sat gazing down at them with affected indifference. She resumed her work with an indescribable expression of sadness; thinking herself unobserved she wept quietly, and a soft flush covered her cheeks. These signs of emotion did not escape Nicolo, who was unobtrusively watching her, and he no longer had any doubt that she had merely been disguising his own name by this transposed spelling. He saw her put out her hand and gently disarrange the letters, and his wild hopes reached their height as she rose, laid aside her sewing and disappeared into her bedroom. He was just about to leave his seat and follow her when Piachi entered and, on inquiring for Elvira was told by one of the maid-servants that she had felt unwell and gone to lie down. Piachi, without seeming particularly alarmed, turned and went to her room to see how she was; and when he returned a quarter of an hour later, announced that she would not appear for dinner, and then did not mention the matter again, Nicolo remembered the many mysterious scenes of this kind that he had witnessed, and felt convinced that he now held the clue to their meaning.

The following morning, as he sat gloating over his new discovery and considering how he might best exploit it, he received a note from Xaviera in which she asked him to come and see her, as she had some interesting news for him about Elvira. Xaviera, as the Bishop's protégée, enjoyed the intimate acquaintance of the Carmelite monks; and since it was to the Carmelite monastery that Nicolo's adoptive mother went to confession, he had no doubt that Xaviera must have succeeded in eliciting some information about the secret history of her feelings which would prove favourable to his unnatural desires. There was, however, an unpleasant surprise in store for him; for Xaviera, after greeting him with an oddly roguish air and drawing him down beside her on to the divan where she was sitting, declared that what she had to tell him was simply that the object of Elvira's love was a man who had already been dead and buried for twelve years. The original of the portrait he had found in her bedroom in the alcove behind the red silk curtain was Aloysius, Marquis of Montferrat; an uncle in Paris in whose house he had been educated had called him Collin, this being later changed in Italy to the nickname Colino; and he was the young Genoese nobleman who had so heroically rescued her from the fire when she was a child and been mortally injured in doing so. Xaviera added that she must ask Nicolo not to make any use of this secret, as it had been entrusted to her in the Carmelite monastery, under the seal of absolute discretion, by someone who himself had no right to it. Nicolo, flushing and turning pale by turns, assured her that she could set her mind at rest; and being quite unable to conceal from her mischievous glances the embarrassment into which this disclosure had flung him, he excused himself on the pretext of having some business and took his hat, his upper lip twitching unpleasantly as he left her.

Humiliation, lust and the desire for revenge now conspired in his mind to engender a deed of unutterable vileness. He well knew that deception would be the only access to Elvira's pure soul; and at the first opportunity Piachi gave him by going for a few days into the country, he prepared to execute the satanic plan on which he had decided. He procured again the very same costume in which he had appeared to Elvira a few months earlier as he was secretly returning late at night from the carnival; and putting on the cloak and doublet and feathered hat of Genoese cut, exactly as the figure in the portrait wore them, he stealthily entered her room just before bedtime. He hung a black cloth over the picture in the alcove, and with a staff in his hand, in the precise posture of the young nobleman on the canvas, awaited Elvira's adoring homage. And his reckoning, sharpened by shameful passion, had been entirely correct; for she presently entered, undressed quietly and calmly, and had no sooner drawn back as usual the silk curtain of the alcove and set eyes on him, than with a cry of "Colino! my beloved!" she fell senseless to the floor. Nicolo stepped out of the alcove; he stood for a moment absorbed in contemplation of her charms and gazed at her delicate figure now suddenly paling in the embrace of death; but presently, since there was no time to be lost, he took her up in his arms, snatched the black cloth from the portrait, and carried her to the bed in the corner of the room. Having done this he went to bolt the door, but found it already locked; and confident that even after recovering her disordered senses she would offer no resistance to the fantastic and supernatural apparition for which she must take him, he now returned to the bed and set about reviving her with burning kisses on her lips and breasts. But the Nemesis that dogs the heels of crime had decreed that Piachi, who was to have been absent, as the wretched Nicolo supposed, for another few days, should chance to return to his house unexpectedly at that very moment. Thinking Elvira would already be asleep, he crept softly along the corridor; and as he always carried the keys with him, he was able to open the door without making a sound and stepped suddenly into the room. Nicolo stood speechless; and as there was no possibility of dissembling his disgraceful intentions, he threw himself at the old man's feet and implored his forgiveness, vowing never to cast eyes upon his wife again. And Piachi did, indeed, feel inclined to deal with the matter discreetly. Bereft of words by something which Elvira whispered to him as she revived in his arms and gazed with horror at her assailant, he merely closed the curtains of her bed, took a whip from the wall, opened the door and pointed to it, indicating thereby to Nicolo in what direction he must now immediately betake himself. But the latter, seeing that nothing was to be gained by show of penitence, behaved at this point in a manner worthy of Tartuffe himself: he suddenly stood up and declared that it was for Piachi to leave the house, for he, Nicolo, was now its owner by deed of gift and he would defend his title to it against all comers. Piachi could scarcely believe his ears; disarmed by this inconceivable piece of effrontery, he put down the whip, took his hat and stick and ran to the house of his old friend, the lawyer Dr Valerio. He rang the bell until a maid opened the door, and on reaching his friend's room collapsed unconscious beside his bed before he could utter a word. The lawyer took him, and later Elvira as well, into his house for the night, and set off in haste next morning to procure the arrest of the abominable Nicolo. But the infernal scoundrel's legal position was strong; and while Piachi vainly sought ways and means to dispossess him of the property over which he had already given him full rights, he had at once gone hotfoot with his deed of settlement to the Carmelite monks and appealed to them for protection against, as he said, the old fool who was now trying to evict him. In the end, after he had consented to marry Xaviera, whom the Bishop wanted taken off his hands, wickedness prevailed, and this prince of the Church was able to induce the authorities to issue a decree confirming Nicolo's title to the property and enjoining Piachi to leave him in possession without further interference.

Only the previous day Piachi had buried the unhappy Elvira, who as a result of the recent episode had fallen into a burning fever and died. Maddened by this double blow he went into the house with the injunction in his pocket, and with rage lending him strength he felled Nicolo, who was of weaker build, to the floor, and crushed out his brains against the wall. No one else in the house noticed his presence until the deed was already done; by the time they found him he was holding Nicolo between his knees and stuffing the injunction into his mouth. Having done so he stood up, surrendered all his weapons, and was then imprisoned, tried, and condemned to death by hanging.

In the Papal State there is a law by which no criminal may be led to his death before he has received absolution. This Piachi, when his life had been declared forfeit, stubbornly refused to do. After all the arguments of religion had been vainly adduced to convince him of the heinousness of his behaviour, he was led out to the gallows in the hope that the sight of the death that awaited him might frighten him into penitence. On one side stood a priest who in a voice like the last trump described to him all the terrors of hell into which his soul was about to be plunged; opposite stood another, holding in his hand the Body of Christ, the sacred means of redemption, and spoke to him of the glorious abodes of eternal peace. "Will you accept the blessed gift of salvation?" they both asked him. "Will you receive the sacrament?" "No," replied Piachi. "Why not?" "I do not want to be saved, I want to go down into the deepest pit of hell, I want to find Nicolo again — for he will not be in heaven — and continue my vengeance on him which I could not finish here to my full satisfaction." And so saying he ascended the ladder and called upon the hangman to perform his duty. In the end the execution had to be stayed and the wretched man taken back to prison, for the law protected him. On three successive days similar attempts were made and every time without avail. On the third day, forced once more to come down from the ladder unhanged, he raised his fists in a gesture of bitter rage and cursed the inhuman law that forbade him to go to hell. He called upon the whole legion of devils to come and fetch him, swore he had no other wish but to be doomed and damned, and vowed he would throttle the first priest who came to hand if by so doing he might get to hell and lay hold of Nicolo again! When this was reported to the Pope, he ordered that Piachi should be executed without absolution; and unaccompanied by any priest, he was strung up very quietly in the Piazza del Popolo.

Translated from the German by David Luke and Nigel Reeves.

There Are No Snakes in Ireland

Frederick Forsyth

Frederick Forsyth

(England, b. 1938)

Popularity is a curse, especially among writers. Those who tell a good story, those who do not believe in the rule ''Take care of the sounds and the sense will take care of itself,'' run the danger of being considered trite. Somerset Maugham, Daphne du Maurier, Rider Haggard . . . the list of derided great writers whose sin, in the eyes of the intelligentsia, is to be entertaining, is endless. Frederick Forsyth, ''the youngest pilot in the Royal Air Force at the age of nineteen,'' went from flying to journalism and from journalism to literature. As a reporter for Reuters in Paris, he researched the basic material that was to become his best-selling novel, *The Day of the Jackal*, saluted by the critics as both immensely readable and immensely unliterary. Undaunted, Forsyth produced other books in the same vein — *The Odessa File, The Dogs of War, The Devil's Alternative*. ''There Are No Snakes in Ireland'' comes from his only collection of short stories, *No Comebacks*. Its title alludes to the legend of St Patrick, Ireland's patron saint, who allegedly rid the country of these emissaries of Satan. With this in mind, the story may be read not only as a brilliant adventure, but also as a subtle, many-faceted allegory.

There Are No Snakes in Ireland

McQueen looked across his desk at the new applicant for a job with some scepticism. He had never employed such a one before. But he was not an unkind man, and if the job-seeker needed the money and was prepared to work, McQueen was not averse to giving him a chance.

"You know it's damn hard work?" he said in his broad Belfast accent.

"Yes, sir," said the applicant.

"It's a quick in-and-out job, ye know. No questions, no pack drill. You'll be working on the lump. Do you know what that means?"

"No, Mr McQueen."

"Well, it means you'll be paid well but you'll be paid in cash. No red tape. Geddit?"

What he meant was there would be no income tax paid, no National Health contributions deducted at source. He might also have added that there would be no National Insurance cover and that the Health and Safety standards would be completely ignored. Quick profits for all were the order of the day, with a fat slice off the top for himself as the contractor. The job-seeker nodded his head to indicate he had "goddit" though in fact he had not. McQueen looked at him speculatively.

"You say you're a medical student, in your last year at the Royal Victoria?" Another nod. "On the summer vacation?"

Another nod. The applicant was evidently one of those students who needed money over and above his grant to put himself through medical school. McQueen, sitting in his dingy Bangor office running a hole-and-corner business as a demolition contractor with assets consisting of a battered truck and a ton of second-hand sledgehammers, considered himself a self-made man and heartily approved of the Ulster Protestant work ethic. He was not one to put down another such thinker, whatever he looked like.

"All right," he said, "you'd better take lodgings here in Bangor. You'll never get from Belfast and back in time each day. We work from seven in the morning until sundown. It's work by the hour, hard but well paid. Mention one word to the authorities and you'll lose the job like shit off a shovel. OK?"

"Yes, sir. Please, when do I start and where?"

"The truck picks the gang up at the main station yard every morning at six-thirty. Be there Monday morning. The gang foreman is Big Billie Cameron. I'll tell him you'll be there."

"Yes, Mr McQueen." The applicant turned to go.

"One last thing," said McQueen, pencil poised. "What's your name?"

"Harkishan Ram Lal," said the student. McQueen looked at his pencil, the list of names in front of him and the student.

"We'll call you Ram," he said, and that was the name he wrote down on the list.

The student walked out into the bright July sunshine of Bangor, on the north coast of County Down, Northern Ireland.

By that Saturday evening he had found himself cheap lodgings in a dingy boarding house halfway up Railway View

Street, the heart of Bangor's bed-and-breakfast land. At least it was convenient to the main station from which the works truck would depart every morning just after sun-up. From the grimy window of his room he could look straight at the side of the shored embankment that carried the trains from Belfast into the station.

It had taken him several tries to get a room. Most of those houses with a B-and-B notice in the window seemed to be fully booked when he presented himself on the doorstep. But then it was true that a lot of casual labour drifted into the town in the height of summer. True also that Mrs McGurk was a Catholic and she still had rooms left.

He spent Sunday morning bringing his belongings over from Belfast, most of them medical textbooks. In the afternoon he lay on his bed and thought of the bright hard light on the brown hills of his native Punjab. In one more year he would be a qualified physician, and after another year of intern work he would return home to cope with the sicknesses of his own people. Such was his dream. He calculated he could make enough money this summer to tide himself through to his finals and after that he would have a salary of his own.

On the Monday morning he rose at a quarter to six at the bidding of his alarm clock, washed in cold water and was in the station yard just after six. There was time to spare. He found an early-opening café and took two cups of black tea. It was his only sustenance. The battered truck, driven by one of the demolition gang, was there at a quarter past six and a dozen men assembled near it. Harkishan Ram Lal did not know whether to approach them to introduce himself, or wait at a distance. He waited.

At twenty-five past the hour the foreman arrived in his own car, parked it down a side road and strode up to the truck. He had McQueen's list in his hand. He glanced at the dozen men, recognized them all and nodded. The Indian approached. The foreman glared at him.

"Is youse the darkie McQueen has put on the job?" he demanded.

Ram Lal stopped in his tracks. "Harkishan Ram Lal," he said. "Yes."

There was no need to ask how Big Billie Cameron had earned his name. He stood 6 feet and 3 inches in his stockings but was wearing enormous nail-studded, steel-toed boots. Arms like tree trunks hung from huge shoulders and his head was surmounted by a shock of ginger hair. Two small, pale-lashed eyes stared down balefully at the slight and wiry Indian. It was plain he was not best pleased. He spat on the ground.

"Well get in the fecking truck," he said.

On the journey out to the work site Cameron sat up in the cab which had no partition dividing it from the back of the lorry, where the dozen labourers sat on two wooden benches down the sides. Ram Lal was near the tailboard next to a small, nut-hard man with bright blue eyes, whose name turned out be Tommy Burns. He seemed friendly.

"Where are youse from?" he asked with genuine curiosity.

"India," said Ram Lal. "The Punjab."

"Well, which?" said Tommy Burns.

Ram Lal smiled. "The Punjab is a part of India," he said.

Burns thought about this for a while. "You Protestant or Catholic?" he asked at length.

"Neither," said Ram Lal patiently. "I am a Hindu."

"You mean you're not a Christian?" asked Burns in amazement.

"No. Mine is the Hindu religion."

"Hey," said Burns to the others, "your man's not a Christian at all." He was not outraged, just curious, like a small child who has come across a new and intriguing toy.

Cameron turned from the cab up front. "Aye," he snarled, "a heathen."

The smile dropped off Ram Lal's face. He stared at the opposite canvas wall of the truck. By now they were well south of Bangor, clattering down the motorway towards Newtownards. After a while Burns began to introduce him to the others. There was a Craig, a Munroe, a Patterson, a Boyd and two Browns. Ram Lal had been long enough in Belfast to recognize the names as being originally Scottish, the sign of the hard Presbyterians who make up the backbone of the Protestant majority of the Six Counties. The men seemed amiable and nodded back at him.

"Have you not got a lunch box, laddie?" asked the elderly man called Patterson.

"No," said Ram Lal, "it was too early to ask my landlady to make one up."

"You'll need lunch," said Burns, "aye, and breakfast. We'll be making tay ourselves on a fire."

"I will make sure to buy a box and bring some food tomorrow," said Ram Lal.

Burns looked at the Indian's rubber-soled soft boots. "Have you not done this kind of work before?" he asked.

Ram Lal shook his head.

"You'll need a pair of heavy boots. To save your feet, you see."

Ram Lal promised he would also buy a pair of heavy ammunition boots from a store if he could find one open late at night. They were through Newtownards and still heading south on the A21 towards the small town of Comber. Craig looked across at him.

"What's your real job?" he asked.

"I'm a medical student at the Royal Victoria in Belfast," said Ram Lal. "I hope to qualify next year."

Tommy Burns was delighted. "That's near to being a real doctor," he said. "Hey, Big Billie, if one of us gets a knock young Ram could take care of it."

Big Billie grunted. "He's not putting a finger on me," he said.

That killed further conversation until they arrived at the work site. The driver had pulled northwest out of Comber and two miles up the Dundonald road he bumped down a track to the right until they came to a stop where the trees ended and saw the building to be demolished.

It was a huge old whiskey distillery, sheer-sided, long derelict. It had been one of two in these parts that had once turned out good Irish whiskey but had gone out of business years before. It stood beside the River Comber, which had once powered its great waterwheel as it flowed down from Dundonald to Comber and on to empty itself in Strangford Lough. The malt had arrived by horse-drawn cart down the track and the barrels of whiskey had left the same way. The sweet water that had powered the machines had also been used in the vats. But the distillery had stood alone, abandoned and empty for years.

Of course the local children had broken in and found it an ideal place to play. Until one had slipped and broken a leg. Then the county council had surveyed it, declared it a hazard and the owner found himself with a compulsory demolition order.

He, scion of an old family of squires who had known better days, wanted the job done as cheaply as possible. That was where McQueen came in. It could be done faster but more expensively with heavy machinery; Big Billie and his team would do it with sledges and crowbars. McQueen had even lined up a deal to sell the best timbers and the hundreds of tons of mature bricks to a jobbing builder. After all, the wealthy nowadays wanted their new houses to have "style" and that meant looking old. So there was a premium on antique sun-bleached old bricks and genuine ancient timber beams to adorn the new-look-old "manor" houses of the top executives. McQueen would do all right.

"Right lads," said Big Billie as the truck rumbled away back to Bangor. "There it is. We'll start with the roof tiles. You know what to do."

The group of men stood beside their pile of equipment. There were great sledgehammers with 7-pound heads; crowbars 6 feet long and over an inch thick; nailbars a yard long with curved split tips for extracting nails; short-handled, heavy-headed lump hammers and a variety of timber saws. The only concessions to human safety were a number of webbing belts with dogclips and hundreds of feet of rope. Ram Lal looked up at the building and swallowed. It was four storeys high and he hated heights. But scaffolding is expensive.

One of the men unbidden went to the building, prised off a plank door, tore it up like a playing card and started a fire. Soon a billycan of water from the river was boiling away and tea was made. They all had their enamel mugs except Ram Lal. He made a mental note to buy that also. It was going to be thirsty, dusty work. Tommy Burns finished his own mug and offered it, refilled, to Ram Lal.

"Do they have tea in India?" he asked.

Ram Lal took the proffered mug. The tea was ready-mixed, sweet and off-white. He hated it.

They worked through the first morning perched high on the roof. The tiles were not to be salvaged, so they tore them off manually and hurled them to the ground away from the river. There was an instruction not to block the river with falling rubble. So it all had to land on the other side of the building, in the long grass, weeds, broom and gorse which covered the area round the distillery. The men were roped together so that if one lost his grip and began to slither down the roof, the next man would take the strain. As the tiles disappeared, great yawning holes appeared between the rafters. Down below them was the floor of the top storey, the malt store.

At ten they came down the rickety internal stairs for breakfast on the grass, with another billycan of tea. Ram Lal ate no breakfast. At two they broke for lunch. The gang tucked into their piles of thick sandwiches. Ram Lal looked at his hands. They were nicked in several places and bleeding. His muscles ached and he was very hungry. He made another mental note about buying some heavy work gloves.

Tommy Burns held up a sandwich from his own box. "Are you not hungry, Ram?" he asked. "Sure, I have enough here."

"What do you think you're doing?" asked Big Billie from where he sat across the circle round the fire.

Burns looked defensive. "Just offering the lad a sandwich," he said.

"Let the darkie bring his own fecking sandwiches," said Cameron. "You look after yourself."

The men looked down at their lunch boxes and ate in

silence. It was obvious no one argued the toss with Big Billie.

"Thank you, I am not hungry," said Ram Lal to Burns. He walked away and sat by the river where he bathed his burning hands.

By sundown when the truck came to collect them half the tiles on the great roof were gone. One more day and they would start on the rafters, work for saw and nailbar.

Throughout the week the work went on, and the once proud building was stripped of its rafters, planks and beams until it stood hollow and open, its gaping windows like open eyes staring at the prospect of its imminent death. Ram Lal was unaccustomed to the arduousness of this kind of labour. His muscles ached endlessly, his hands were blistered, but he toiled on for the money he needed so badly.

He had acquired a tin lunch box, enamel mug, hard boots and a pair of heavy gloves, which no one else wore. Their hands were hard enough from years of manual work. Throughout the week Big Billie Cameron needled him without let-up, giving him the hardest work and positioning him on the highest points once he had learned Ram Lal hated heights. The Punjabi bit on his anger because he needed the money. The crunch came on the Saturday.

The timbers were gone and they were working on the masonry. The simplest way to bring the edifice down away from the river would have been to plant explosive charges in the corners of the side wall facing the open clearing. But dynamite was out of the question. It would have required special licences in Northern Ireland of all places, and that would have alerted the tax man. McQueen and all his gang would have been required to pay substantial sums in income tax, and McQueen in National Insurance contributions. So they were chipping the walls down in square-yard chunks, standing hazardously on sagging floors as the supporting walls splintered and cracked under the hammers.

During lunch Cameron walked round the building a couple of times and came back to the circle round the fire. He began to describe how they were going to bring down a sizable chunk of one outer wall at third-floor level. He returned to Ram Lal.

"I want you up on the top there," he said. "When it starts to go, kick it outwards."

Ram Lal looked up at the section of wall in question. A great crack ran along the bottom of it.

"That brickwork is going to fall at any moment," he said evenly. "Anyone sitting on top there is going to come down with it."

Cameron stared at him, his face suffusing, his eyes pink with rage where they should have been white. "Don't you tell me my job; you do as you're told, you stupid fecking nigger." He turned and stalked away.

Ram Lal rose to his feet. When his voice came, it was in a hard-edged shout. "*Mister Cameron . . .*"

Cameron turned in amazement. The men sat open-mouthed. Ram Lal walked slowly up to the big ganger.

"Let us get one thing plain," said Ram Lal, and his voice carried clearly to everyone else in the clearing. "I am from the Punjab in northern India. I am also a Kshatria, member of the warrior caste. I may not have enough money to pay for my medical studies, but my ancestors were soldiers and princes, rulers and scholars, two thousand years ago when yours were crawling on all fours dressed in skins. Please do not insult me any further."

Big Billie Cameron stared down at the Indian student. The whites of his eyes had turned a bright red. The other labourers sat in stunned amazement.

"Is that so?" said Cameron quietly. "Is that so, now? Well, things are a bit different now, you black bastard. So what are you going to do about that?"

On the last word he swung his arm, open-palmed, and his hand crashed into the side of Ram Lal's face. The youth was thrown bodily to the ground several feet away. His head sang. He heard Tommy Burns call out, "Stay down laddie. Big Billie will kill you if you get up."

Ram Lal looked up into the sunlight. The giant stood over him, fists bunched. He realized he had not a chance in combat against the big Ulsterman. Feelings of shame and humiliation flooded over him. His ancestors had ridden, sword and lance in hand, across plains a hundred times bigger than these six counties, conquering all before them.

Ram Lal closed his eyes and lay still. After several seconds he heard the big man move away. A low conversation started among the others. He squeezed his eyes tighter shut to hold back the tears of shame. In the blackness he saw the baking plains of the Punjab and men riding over them; proud, fierce men, hook-nosed, bearded, turbaned, black-eyed, the warriors from the Land of Five Rivers.

Once, long ago in the world's morning, Iskander of Macedon had ridden over these plains with his hot and hungry eyes; Alexander, the young god, whom they called The Great, who at twenty-five had wept because there were no more worlds to conquer. These riders were the descendants of his captains, and the ancestors of Harkishan Ram Lal.

He was lying in the dust as they rode by, and they looked down at him in passing. As they rode each of them mouthed one single word to him. Vengeance.

Ram Lal picked himself up in silence. It was done, and what still had to be done had to be done. That was the way of his people. He spent the rest of the day working in complete silence. He spoke to no one and no one spoke to him.

That evening in his room he began his preparations as night was about to fall. He cleared away the brush and comb from the battered dressing table and removed also the soiled doily and the mirror from its stand. He took his book of the Hindu religion and from it cut a page-sized portrait of the great goddess Shakti, she of power and justice. This he pinned to the wall above the dressing table to convert it into a shrine.

He had bought a bunch of flowers from a seller in front of the main station, and these had been woven into a garland. To one side of the portrait of the goddess he placed a shallow bowl half-filled with sand, and in the sand stuck a candle which he lit. From his suitcase he took a cloth roll and extracted half a dozen joss sticks. Taking a cheap, narrow-necked vase from the bookshelf, he placed them in it and lit the ends. The sweet, heady odour of the incense began to fill the room. Outside, big thunderheads rolled up from the sea.

When his shrine was ready he stood before it, head bowed, the garland in his fingers, and began to pray for guidance. The first rumble of thunder rolled over Bangor. He used not the modern Punjabi but the ancient Sanskrit, language of prayer. "*Devi Shakti . . . Maa* . . . Goddess Shakti . . . great mother . . ."

The thunder crashed again and the first raindrops fell. He plucked the first flower and placed it in front of the portrait of Shakti.

"I have been grievously wronged. I ask vengeance upon the wrongdoer . . ." He plucked the second flower and put it beside the first.

He prayed for an hour while the rain came down. It drummed on the tiles above his head, streamed past the window behind him. He finished praying as the storm subsided. He needed to know what form the retribution should take. He needed the goddess to send him a sign.

When he had finished, the joss sticks had burned themselves out and the room was thick with their scent. The candle guttered low. The flowers all lay on the lacquered surface of the dressing table in front of the portrait. Shakti stared back at him unmoved.

He turned and walked to the window to look out. The rain had stopped but everything beyond the panes dripped water. As he watched, a dribble of rain sprang from the guttering above the window and a trickle ran down the dusty glass, cutting a path through the grime. Because of the dirt it did not run straight but meandered sideways, drawing his eye farther and farther to the corner of the window as he followed its path. When it stopped he was staring at the corner of his room, where his dressing gown hung on a nail.

He noticed that during the storm the dressing-gown cord had slipped and fallen to the floor. It lay coiled upon itself, one knotted end hidden from view, the other lying visible on the carpet. Of the dozen tassels only two were exposed, like a forked tongue. The coiled dressing-gown cord resembled nothing so much as a snake in the corner. Ram Lal understood. The next day he took the train to Belfast to see the Sikh.

Ranjit Singh was also a medical student, but he was more fortunate. His parents were rich and sent him a handsome allowance. He received Ram Lal in his well-furnished room at the hostel.

"I have received word from home," said Ram Lal. "My father is dying."

"I am sorry," said Ranjit Singh, "you have my sympathies."

"He asks to see me. I am his first born. I should return."

"Of course," said Singh. The first-born son should always be by his father when he dies.

"It is a matter of the air fare," said Ram Lal. "I am working and making good money. But I do not have enough. If you will lend me the balance I will continue working when I return and repay you."

Sikhs are no strangers to moneylending if the interest is right and repayment secure. Ranjit Singh promised to withdraw the money from the bank on Monday morning.

That Sunday evening Ram Lal visited Mr McQueen at his home at Groomsport. The contractor was in front of his television set with a can of beer at his elbow. It was his favourite way to spend a Sunday evening. But he turned the sound down as Ram Lal was shown in by his wife.

"It is about my father," said Ram Lal. "He is dying."

"Oh, I'm sorry to hear that, laddie," said McQueen.

"I should go to him. The first-born son should be with his father at this time. It is the custom of our people."

McQueen had a son in Canada whom he had not seen for seven years.

"Aye," he said, "that seems right and proper."

"I have borrowed the money for the air fare," said Ram Lal. "If I went tomorrow I could be back by the end of the week. The point is, Mr McQueen, I need the job more than ever now; to repay the loan and for my studies next term. If I am back by the weekend, will you keep the job open for me?"

"All right," said the contractor. "I can't pay you for the time you're away. Nor keep the job open for a further week. But if you're back by the weekend, you can go back to work. Same terms, mind."

"Thank you," said Ram, "you are very kind."

He retained his room in Railway View Street but spent the night at his hostel in Belfast. On the Monday morning he accompanied Ranjit Singh to the bank where the Sikh withdrew the necessary money and gave it to the Hindu. Ram took a taxi to Aldergrove airport and the shuttle to London where he bought an economy-class ticket on the next flight to India. Twenty-four hours later he touched down in the blistering heat of Bombay.

On the Wednesday he found what he sought in the teeming bazaar at Grant Road Bridge. Mr Chatterjee's Tropical Fish and Reptile Emporium was almost deserted when the young student, with his textbook on reptiles under his arm, wandered in. He found the old proprietor sitting near the back of his shop in half-darkness, surrounded by his tanks of fish and glass-fronted cases in which his snakes and lizards dozed through the hot day.

Mr Chatterjee was no stranger to the academic world. He supplied several medical centres with samples for study and dissection, and occasionally filled a lucrative order from abroad. He nodded his white-bearded head knowledgeably as the student explained what he sought.

"Ah yes," said the old Gujerati merchant, "I know the snake. You are in luck. I have one, but a few days arrived from Rajputana."

He led Ram Lal into his private sanctum and the two men stared silently through the glass of the snake's new home.

Echis carinatus, said the textbook, but of course the book had been written by an Englishman, who had used the Latin nomenclature. In English, the saw-scaled viper, smallest and deadliest of all his lethal breed.

Wide distribution, said the textbook, being found from West Africa eastwards and northwards to Iran, and on to

India and Pakistan. Very adaptable, able to acclimatize to almost any environment, from the moist bush of western Africa to the cold hills of Iran in winter to the baking hills of India.

Something stirred beneath the leaves in the box.

In size, said the textbook, between 9 and 13 inches long and very slim. Olive brown in colour with a few paler spots, sometimes hardly distinguishable, and a faint undulating darker line down the side of the body. Nocturnal in dry, hot weather, seeking cover during the heat of the day.

The leaves in the box rustled again and a tiny head appeared.

Exceptionally dangerous to handle, said the textbook, causing more deaths than even the more famous cobra, largely because of its size which makes it so easy to touch unwittingly with hand or foot. The author of the book had added a footnote to the effect that the small but lethal snake mentioned by Kipling in his marvellous story "Rikki-Tikki-Tavy" was almost certainly not the krait, which is about 2 feet long, but more probably the saw-scaled viper. The author was obviously pleased to have caught out the great Kipling in a matter of accuracy.

In the box, a little black forked tongue flickered towards the two Indians beyond the glass.

Very alert and irritable, the long-gone English naturalist had concluded his chapter on *Echis carinatus*. Strikes quickly without warning. The fangs are so small they make a virtually unnoticeable puncture, like two tiny thorns. There is no pain, but death is almost inevitable, usually taking between two and four hours, depending on the bodyweight of the victim and the level of his physical exertions at the time and afterwards. Cause of death is invariably a brain haemorrhage.

"How much do you want for him?" whispered Ram Lal.

The old Gujerati spread his hands helplessly. "Such a prime specimen," he said regretfully, "and so hard to come by. Five hundred rupees."

Ram Lal clinched the deal at 350 rupees and took the snake away in a jar.

For his journey back to London Ram Lal purchased a box of cigars, which he emptied of their contents and in whose lid he punctured twenty small holes for air. The tiny viper, he knew, would need no food for a week and no water for two or three days. It could breathe on an infinitesimal supply of air, so he wrapped the cigar box, resealed and with the viper inside it among his leaves, in several towels whose thick sponginess would contain enough air even inside a suitcase.

He had arrived with a handgrip, but he bought a cheap fibre suitcase and packed it with clothes from market stalls, the cigar box going in the centre. It was only minutes before he left his hotel for Bombay airport that he closed and locked the case. For the flight back to London he checked the suitcase into the hold of the Boeing airliner. His hand baggage was searched, but it contained nothing of interest.

The Air India jet landed at London Heathrow on Friday morning and Ram Lal joined the long queue of Indians trying to get into Britain. He was able to prove he was a medical student and not an immigrant, and was allowed through quite quickly. He even reached the luggage carousel as the first suitcases were tumbling onto it, and saw his own in the first two dozen. He took it to the toilet, where he extracted the cigar box and put it in his handgrip.

In the Nothing-to-Declare channel he was stopped all the same, but it was his suitcase that was ransacked. The customs officer glanced in his shoulder bag and let him pass. Ram Lal crossed Heathrow by courtesy bus to Number One Building and caught the midday shuttle to Belfast. He was in Bangor by teatime and able at last to examine his import.

He took a sheet of glass from the bedside table and slipped it carefully between the lid of the cigar box and its deadly contents before opening wide. Through the glass he saw the viper going round and round inside. It paused and stared with angry black eyes back at him. He pulled the lid shut, withdrawing the pane of glass quickly as the box top came down.

"Sleep, little friend," he said, "if your breed ever sleep. In the morning you will do Shakti's bidding for her."

Before dark he bought a small screw-top jar of coffee and

poured the contents into a china pot in his room. In the morning, using his heavy gloves, he transferred the viper from the box to the jar. The enraged snake bit his glove once, but he did not mind. It would have recovered its venom by midday. For a moment he studied the snake, coiled and cramped inside the glass coffee jar, before giving the top a last, hard twist and placing it in his lunch box. Then he went to catch the works truck.

Big Billie Cameron had a habit of taking off his jacket the moment he arrived at the work site, and hanging it on a convenient nail or twig. During the lunch break, as Ram Lal had observed, the giant foreman never failed to go to his jacket after eating, and from the right-hand pocket extract his pipe and tobacco pouch. The routine did not vary. After a satisfying pipe, he would knock out the dottle, rise and say, "Right, lads, back to work," as he dropped his pipe back into the pocket of his jacket. By the time he turned round everyone had to be on their feet.

Ram Lal's plan was simple but foolproof. During the morning he would slip the snake into the right-hand pocket of the hanging jacket. After his sandwiches the bullying Cameron would rise from the fire, go to his jacket and plunge his hand into the pocket. The snake would do what great Shakti had ordered that he be brought halfway across the world to do. It would be he, the viper, not Ram Lal, who would be the Ulsterman's executioner.

Cameron would withdraw his hand with an oath from the pocket, the viper hanging from his finger, its fangs deep in the flesh. Ram Lal would leap up, tear the snake away, throw it to the ground and stamp upon its head. It would by then be harmless, its venom expended. Finally, with a gesture of disgust he, Ram Lal, would hurl the dead viper far into the River Comber, which would carry all evidence away to the sea. There might be suspicion, but that was all there would ever be.

Shortly after eleven o'clock, on the excuse of fetching a fresh sledgehammer, Harkishan Ram Lal opened his lunch box, took out the coffee jar, unscrewed the lid and shook the contents into the right-hand pocket of the hanging jacket. Within sixty seconds he was back at his work, his act unnoticed.

During lunch he found it hard to eat. The men sat as usual in a circle round the fire; the dry old timber baulks crackled and spat, the billycan bubbled above them. The men joshed and joked as ever, while Big Billie munched his way through the pile of doorstep sandwiches his wife had prepared for him. Ram Lal had made a point of choosing a place in the circle near to the jacket. He forced himself to eat. In his chest his heart was pounding and the tension in him rose steadily.

Finally Big Billie crumpled the paper of his eaten sandwiches, threw it in the fire and belched. He rose with a grunt and walked towards his jacket. Ram Lal turned his head to watch. The other men took no notice. Billie Cameron reached his jacket and plunged his hand into the right-hand pocket. Ram Lal held his breath. Cameron's hand rummaged for several seconds and then withdrew his pipe and pouch. He began to fill the bowl with fresh tobacco. As he did so he caught Ram Lal staring at him.

"What are youse looking at?" he demanded belligerently.

"Nothing," said Ram Lal, and turned to face the fire. But he could not stay still. He rose and stretched, contriving to half turn as he did so. From the corner of his eye he saw Cameron replace the pouch in the pocket and again withdraw his hand with a box of matches in it. The foreman lit his pipe and pulled contentedly. He strolled back to the fire.

Ram Lal resumed his seat and stared at the flames in disbelief. Why, he asked himself, why had great Shakti done this to him? The snake had been her tool, her instrument brought at her command. But she had held it back, refused to use her own implement of retribution. He turned and sneaked another glance at the jacket. Deep down in the lining at the very hem, on the extreme left-hand side, something stirred and was still. Ram Lal closed his eyes in shock. A hole, a tiny hole in the lining, had undone all his planning. He worked the rest of the afternoon in a daze of indecision and worry.

On the truck ride back to Bangor, Big Billie Cameron sat up front as usual, but in view of the heat folded his jacket and put it on his knees. In front of the station Ram Lal saw him throw the still-folded jacket onto the back seat of his car and drive away. Ram Lal caught up with Tommy Burns as the little man waited for his bus.

"Tell me," he asked, "does Mr Cameron have a family?"

"Sure," said the little labourer innocently, "a wife and two children."

"Does he live far from here?" said Ram Lal. "I mean, he drives a car."

"Not far," said Burns, "up on the Kilcooley estate. Ganaway Gardens, I think. Going visiting are you?"

"No, no," said Ram Lal, "see you Monday."

Back in his room Ram Lal stared at the impassive image of the goddess of justice.

"I did not mean to bring death to his wife and children," he told her. "They have done nothing to me."

The goddess from far away stared back and gave no reply.

Harkishan Ram Lal spent the rest of the weekend in an agony of anxiety. That evening he walked to the Kilcooley housing estate on the ring road and found Ganaway Gardens. It lay just off Owenroe Gardens and opposite Woburn Walk. At the corner of Woburn Walk there was a telephone kiosk, and here he waited for an hour, pretending to make a call, while he watched the short street across the road. He thought he spotted Big Billie Cameron at one of the windows and noted the house.

He saw a teenage girl come out of it and walk away to join some friends. For a moment he was tempted to accost her and tell her what demon slept inside her father's jacket, but he dared not.

Shortly before dusk a woman came out of the house carrying a shopping basket. He followed her down to the Clandeboye shopping centre, which was open late for those who took their wage packets on a Saturday. The woman he thought to be Mrs Cameron entered Stewarts supermarket and the Indian student trailed round the shelves behind her, trying to pluck up the courage to approach her and reveal the danger in her house. Again his nerve failed him. He might, after all, have the wrong woman, even be mistaken about the house. In that case they would take him away as a madman.

He slept ill that night, his mind racked by visions of the saw-scaled viper coming out of its hiding place in the jacket to slither, silent and deadly, through the sleeping council house.

On the Sunday he again haunted the Kilcooley estate, and firmly identified the house of the Cameron family. He saw Big Billie clearly in the back garden. By mid-afternoon he was attracting attention locally and knew he must either walk boldly up to the front door and admit what he had done, or depart and leave all in the hands of the goddess. The thought of facing the terrible Cameron with the news of what deadly danger had been brought so close to his children was too much. He walked back to Railway View Street.

On Monday morning the Cameron family rose at a quarter to six, a bright and sunny August morning. By six the four of them were at breakfast in the tiny kitchen at the back of the house, the son, daughter and wife in their dressing gowns, Big Billie dressed for work. His jacket was where it had spent the weekend, in a closet in the hallway.

Just after six his daughter Jenny rose, stuffing a piece of marmaladed toast into her mouth.

"I'm away to wash," she said.

"Before ye go, girl, get my jacket from the press," said her father, working his way through a plate of cereal. The girl reappeared a few seconds later with the jacket, held by the collar. She proffered it to her father. He hardly looked up.

"Hang it behind the door," he said. The girl did as she was bid, but the jacket had no hanging tab and the hook was no rusty nail but a smooth chrome affair. The jacket hung for a moment, then fell to the kitchen floor. Her father looked up as she left the room.

"Jenny," he shouted, "pick the damn thing up."

No one in the Cameron household argued with the head of the family. Jenny came back, picked up the jacket and hung it more firmly. As she did, something thin and dark slipped from its folds and slithered into the corner with a dry rustle across the linoleum. She stared at it in horror.

"Dad, what's that in your jacket?"

Big Billie Cameron paused, a spoonful of cereal halfway to his mouth. Mrs Cameron turned from the cooker. Fourteen year-old Bobby ceased buttering a piece of toast and stared. The small creature lay curled in the corner by the row of cabinets, tight-bunched, defensive, glaring back at the world, tiny tongue flickering fast.

"Lord save us, it's a snake," said Mrs Cameron.

"Don't be a bloody fool, woman. Don't you know there are no snakes in Ireland? Everyone knows that," said her husband. He put down the spoon. "What is it, Bobby?"

Though a tyrant inside and outside his house, Big Billie had a grudging respect for the knowledge of his young son, who was good at school and was being taught many strange things. The boy stared at the snake through his owlish glasses.

"It must be a slowworm, Dad," he said. "They had some at school last term for the biology class. Brought them in for dissection. From across the water."

"It doesn't look like a worm to me," said his father.

"It isn't really a worm," said Bobby. "It's a lizard with no legs."

"Then why do they call it a worm?" asked his truculent father.

"I don't know," said Bobby.

"Then what the hell are you going to school for?"

"Will it bite?" asked Mrs Cameron fearfully.

"Not at all," said Bobby. "It's harmless."

"Kill it," said Cameron senior, "and throw it in the dustbin."

His son rose from the table and removed one of his slippers, which he held like a flyswat in one hand. He was advancing, bare-ankled, towards the corner, when his father changed his mind. Big Billie looked up from his plate with a gleeful smile.

"Hold on a minute, just hold on there, Bobby," he said, "I have an idea. Woman, get me a jar."

"What kind of a jar?" asked Mrs Cameron.

"How should I know what kind of a jar? A jar with a lid on it."

Mrs Cameron sighed, skirted the snake and opened a cupboard. She examined her store of jars.

"There's a jamjar, with dried peas in it," she said.

"Put the peas somewhere else and give me the jar," commanded Cameron. She passed him the jar.

"What are you going to do, Dad?" asked Bobby.

"There's a darkie we have at work. A heathen man. He comes from a land with a lot of snakes in it. I have in mind to have some fun with him. A wee joke, like. Pass me that oven glove, Jenny."

"You'll not need a glove," said Bobby. "He can't bite you."

"I'm not touching the dirty thing," said Cameron.

"He's not dirty, said Bobby. "They're very clean creatures."

"You're a fool, boy, for all your school learning. Does the Good Book not say, 'On thy belly shalt thou go, and dust shalt thou eat . . .'? Aye, and more than dust, no doubt. I'll not touch him with me hand."

Jenny passed her father the oven glove. Open jamjar in his left hand, right hand protected by the glove, Big Billie Cameron stood over the viper. Slowly his right hand descended. When it dropped, it was fast; but the small snake was faster. Its tiny fangs went harmlessly into the padding of the glove at the centre of the palm. Cameron did not notice, for the act was masked from his view by his own hands. In a trice the snake was inside the jamjar and the lid was on. Through the glass they watched it wriggle furiously.

"I hate them, harmless or not," said Mrs Cameron. "I'll

thank you to get it out of the house."

"I'll be doing that right now," said her husband, "for I'm late as it is."

He slipped the jamjar into his shoulder bag, already containing his lunch box, stuffed his pipe and pouch into the right-hand pocket of his jacket and took both out to the car. He arrived at the station yard five minutes late and was surprised to find the Indian student staring at him fixedly.

"I suppose he wouldn't have the second sight," thought Big Billie as they trundled south to Newtownards and Comber.

By mid-morning all the gang had been let into Big Billie's secret joke on pain of a thumping if they let on to "the darkie." There was no chance of that; assured that the slowworm was perfectly harmless, they too thought it a good legpull. Only Ram Lal worked on in ignorance, consumed by his private thoughts and worries.

At the lunch break he should have suspected something. The tension was palpable. The men sat in a circle around the fire as usual, but the conversation was stilted and had he not been so preoccupied he would have noticed the half-concealed grins and the looks darted in his direction. He did not notice. He placed his own lunch box between his knees and opened it. Coiled between the sandwiches and the apple, head back to strike, was the viper.

The Indian's scream echoed across the clearing, just ahead of the roar of laughter from the labourers. Simultaneously with the scream, the lunch box flew high in the air as he threw it away from himself with all his strength. All the contents of the box flew in a score of directions, landing in the long grass, the broom and gorse all around them.

Ram Lal was on his feet, shouting. The gangers rolled helplessly in their mirth, Big Billie most of all. He had not had such a laugh in months.

"It's a snake," screamed Ram Lal, "a poisonous snake. Get out of here, all of you. It's deadly."

The laughter redoubled; the men could not contain themselves. The reaction of the joke's victim surpassed all their expectations.

"Please, believe me. It's a snake, a deadly snake."

Big Billie's face was suffused. He wiped tears from his eyes, seated across the clearing from Ram Lal, who was standing looking wildly round.

"You ignorant darkie," he gasped, "don't you know? There are no snakes in Ireland. Understand? There aren't any."

His sides ached with laughing and he leaned back in the grass, his hands behind him to support him. He failed to notice the two pricks, like tiny thorns, that went into the vein on the inside of the right wrist.

The joke was over and the hungry men tucked into their lunches. Harkishan Ram Lal reluctantly took his seat, constantly glancing around him, a mug of steaming tea held ready, eating only with his left hand, staying clear of the long grass. After lunch they returned to work. The old distillery was almost down, the mountains of rubble and savable timbers lying dusty under the August sun.

At half past three Big Billie Cameron stood up from his work, rested on his pick and passed a hand across his forehead. He licked at the slight swelling on the inside of his wrist, then started work again. Five minutes later he straightened up again.

"I'm not feeling so good," he told Patterson, who was next to him. "I'm going to take a spell in the shade."

He sat under a tree for a while and then held his head in his hands. At a quarter past four, still clutching his splitting head, he gave one convulsion and toppled sideways. It was several minutes before Tommy Burns noticed him. He walked across and called to Patterson.

"Big Billie's sick," he called. "He won't answer me."

The gang broke and came over to the tree in whose shade the foreman lay. His sightless eyes were staring at the grass a few inches from his face. Patterson bent over him. He had been long enough in the labouring business to have seen a few dead ones.

"Ram," he said, "you have medical training. What do you think?"

Ram Lal did not need to make an examination, but he did. When he straightened up he said nothing, but Patterson understood.

"Stay here all of you," he said, taking command. "I'm going to phone an ambulance and call McQueen." He set off down the track to the main road.

The ambulance got there first, half an hour later. It reversed down the track and two men heaved Cameron onto a stretcher. They took him away to Newtownards General Hospital, which had the nearest casualty unit, and there the foreman was logged in as DOA — dead on arrival. An extremely worried McQueen arrived thirty minutes after that.

Because of the unknown circumstance of the death an autopsy had to be performed and it was, by the North Down area pathologist, in the Newtownards municipal mortuary to which the body had been transferred. That was on the Tuesday. By that evening the pathologist's report was on its way to the office of the coroner for North Down, in Belfast.

The report said nothing extraordinary. The deceased had been a man of forty-one years, big-built and immensely strong. There were upon the body various minor cuts and abrasions, mainly on the hands and wrists, quite consistent with the job of navvy, and none of these were in any way associated with the cause of death. The latter, beyond a doubt, had been a massive brain haemorrhage, itself probably caused by extreme exertion in conditions of great heat.

Possessed of this report, the coroner would normally not hold an inquest, being able to issue a certificate of death by natural causes to the registrar at Bangor. But there was something Harkishan Ram Lal did not know.

Big Billie Cameron had been a leading member of the Bangor council of the outlawed Ulster Volunteer Force, the hard-line Protestant paramilitary organization. The computer at Lurgan, into which all deaths in the province of Ulster, however innocent, are programmed, threw this out and someone in Lurgan picked up the phone to call the Royal Ulster Constabulary at Castlereagh.

Someone there called the coroner's office in Belfast, and a formal inquest was ordered. In Ulster death must not only be accidental; it must be seen to be accidental. For certain people, at least. The inquest was in the Town Hall at Bangor on the Wednesday. It meant a lot of trouble for McQueen, for the Inland Revenue attended. So did two quiet men of extreme Loyalist persuasion from the UVF council. They sat at the back. Most of the dead man's workmates sat near the front, a few feet from Mrs Cameron.

Only Patterson was called to give evidence. He related the events of the Monday, prompted by the coroner, and as there was no dispute none of the other labourers was called, not even Ram Lal. The coroner read the pathologist's report aloud and it was clear enough. When he had finished, he summed up before giving his verdict.

"The pathologist's report is quite unequivocal. We have heard from Mr Patterson of the events of that lunch break, of the perhaps rather foolish prank played by the deceased upon the Indian student. It would seem that Mr Cameron was so amused that he laughed himself almost to the verge of apoplexy. The subsequent heavy labour with pick and shovel in the blazing sun did the rest, provoking the rupture of a large blood vessel in the brain or, as the pathologist puts it in more medical language, a cerebral haemorrhage. This court extends its sympathy to the widow and her children, and finds that Mr William Cameron died of accidental causes."

Outside on the lawns that spread before Bangor Town Hall McQueen talked to his navvies.

"I'll stand fair by you, lads," he said. "The job's still on, but I can't afford not to deduct tax and all the rest, not with the Revenue breathing down my neck. The funeral's tomorrow, you can take the day off. Those who want to go on can report on Friday."

Harkishan Ram Lal did not attend the funeral. While it

was in progress at the Bangor cemetery he took a taxi back to Comber and asked the driver to wait on the road while he walked down the track. The driver was a Bangor man and had heard about the death of Cameron.

"Going to pay your respects on the spot, are you?" he asked.

"In a way," said Ram Lal.

"That the manner of your people?" asked the driver.

"You could say so," said Ram Lal.

"Aye, well, I'll not say it's any better or worse than our way, by the graveside," said the driver, and prepared to read his paper while he waited.

Harkishan Ram Lal walked down the track to the clearing and stood where the camp fire had been. He looked around at the long grass, the broom and the gorse in its sandy soil.

"*Visha serp*," he called out to the hidden viper. "O venomous snake, can you hear me? You have done what I brought you so far from the hills of Rajputana to achieve. But you were supposed to die. I should have killed you myself, had it all gone as I planned, and thrown your foul carcass in the river.

"Are you listening, deadly one? Then hear this. You may live a little longer but then you will die, as all things die. And you will die alone, without a female with which to mate, because there are no snakes in Ireland."

The saw-scaled viper did not hear him, or if it did, gave no hint of understanding. Deep in its hole in the warm sand beneath him, it was busy, totally absorbed in doing what nature commanded it must do.

At the base of the snake's tail are two overlapping plate-scales which obscure the cloaca. The viper's tail was erect, the body throbbed in ancient rhythm. The plates were parted, and from the cloaca, one by one, each an inch long in its transparent sac, each as deadly at birth as its parent, she was bringing her dozen babies into the world.

The Great Electrical Revolution

Ken Mitchell

Ken Mitchell

(Canada, b. 1940)

Ken Mitchell's "The Great Electrical Revolution" was a gift from Hal Wake, associate producer at CBC's "Morningside" radio show. I had imagined that I would find a bumper crop of revenge stories in Canadian literature, especially in the irate literature of Quebec. Much to my surprise, the search led nowhere (or almost nowhere; I found and discarded a few stories which I simply did not like). I concluded that, in fact, an interesting essay might be written on why the theme of revenge is *not* popular in Canadian literature.

Ken Mitchell, best known for such plays as *Heroes*, and *Cruel Tears*, is a careful chronicler of life on the Canadian Praries, gifted with a Marx Brothers sense of humour. In "The Great Electrical Revolution" this humour comes from the contrast between the mythical pioneer spirit and the intimate reality of the settlers, from the fate of a man who is given a vast tract of land and who discovers too late that he suffers from agoraphobia. It is a story of revenge sought by downcast heroes against the tedious officials of society, heroes who when faced with unavoidable, foreseeable defeat, achieve in their efforts a certain epic grandeur.

The Great Electrical Revolution

I was only a little guy in 1937, but I can remember Grandad being out of work. Nobody had any money to pay him, and as he said, there wasn't much future in brick-laying as a charity. So mostly he just sat around in his suite above the hardware store, listening to his radio. We *all* listened to it when there was nothing else to do, which was most of the time, unless you happened to be going to school like me. Grandad stuck right there through it all — soap operas, weather reports, and quiz shows — unless he got a bit of cash from somewhere. Then he and Uncle Fred would go downtown to the beer parlour at the King William Hotel.

Grandad and Grandma came from the old country long before I was born. When they arrived in Moose Jaw, all they had was three children — Uncle Fred, Aunt Thecla, and my Dad; a trunk full of working clothes; and a twenty-six-pound post maul for putting up fences to keep "rogues" off Grandad's land. Rogues meant Orangemen, cattle rustlers, capitalists, and Indians. All the way on the train from Montreal, he glared out the Pullman window at the endless flat, saying to his family:

"I came here for land, b'Christ, and none of 'em's goin' to sly it on me."

He had sworn to carve a mighty estate from the raw Saskatchewan prairie, although he had never so much as picked up a garden hoe in his life before leaving Dublin.

When he stepped off the train at the C.P.R. station in Moose Jaw, it looked like he was thinking of tearing it down and seeding the site to oats. It was two o'clock in the morning but he kept striding up and down the lobby of the station, dressed in his good wool suit with the vest, puffing his chest like a bantam rooster in a chicken run. My dad and Uncle Fred and Aunt Thecla sat on the trunk, while Grandma pleaded with him to go and find them a place to stay. (It was only later they realized he was afraid to step outside the station.) He finally quit strutting long enough to get a porter to carry their trunk to a hotel across the street.

The next morning they went to the government land office to secure their homestead. Then Grandad rented a democrat and took my Dad and Uncle Fred out to inspect the land they had come halfway around the world to find. Grandma and Aunt Thecla were told to stay in the hotel room and thank the Blessed Virgin for deliverance. They were still offering prayers three hours later, when Grandad burst back into the room, his eyes wild and his face pale and quivering.

"Sweet Jesus Christ!" he shouted at them. "There's too much of it! There's just too damn much of it out there." He ran around the room several times, knocking against the walls and moaning, "Miles and miles of nothing but miles and miles!" He collapsed onto one of the beds, and lay staring at the ceiling.

"It 'ud drive us witless in a week!"

The two boys came in and told the story of the expedition. Grandad had started out fine, perhaps just a bit nervous. But the further they went from the town, the more agitated and wild-eyed he became. Soon he stopped urging the horse along and asked it to stop. They were barely five miles from town when they turned around and came back, with Uncle Fred driving. Grandad could only crouch on the floor of the democrat, trying to hide from the enormous sky, and whispering at Fred to go faster. He'd come four thousand miles to the wide open spaces — only to discover he suffered from agoraphobia.

That was his last excursion onto the open prairie. (He did make one special trip to Bulkhead in 1928 to fix Aunt Thecla's chimney, but that was a family favour. Even then Uncle Fred had to drive him there in an enclosed Ford sedan in the middle of the night, with newspapers taped to the windows so he couldn't see out.) He abandoned the dream of a country manor. There was nothing he could do but take up bricklaying again in Moose Jaw, where there were trees and tall buildings to protect him from the vastness. Maybe it was a fortunate turn of fate; certainly he prospered from then until the Depression hit, about the time I was born.

Yet — Grandad always felt guilty about not settling on the land. It was his conscience that prompted him to send my Dad to work at a cattle ranch in the hills, the day after he turned sixteen. He married Aunt Thecla off to a Lutheran farmer at Bulkhead who threshed about five hundred acres of wheat every fall. Uncle Fred was the eldest and an apprentice bricklayer, so he stayed in town and lived with Grandad and Grandma in the suite above the hardware store.

I don't remember much about the cattle ranch my father eventually took over, except whirls of dust and skinny animals dragging themselves from one side of the range to the other. Finally there were no more cattle, and no money to buy more, and nothing to feed them if we *did* buy them, except wild foxtail and Russian thistle. So we moved into Moose Jaw with Grandad and Grandma, and went on relief. It was better than the ranch, where there was nothing to do but watch tumbleweeds roll through the yard. We would have had to travel into town to collect our salted fish and government pork anyway. Grandad was happy to have us, because when my Dad went down to the railway yard to get our ration, he collected Grandad's too. My Dad never complained about waiting in line for a handout, but Grandad would have starved to death first. "Damned government drives us all to the edge," he'd say. "Then they want us to queue up for the God-damned swill they're poisoning us with."

That was when we spent so much time listening to Grandad's radio, a great slab of black walnut cabinet he had swindled, so he thought, from a second-hand dealer on River Street. An incandescent green bulb glowed in the centre of it when the tubes were warming up. There was a row of knobs with elaborate-looking initials and a dial with the names of cities like Tokyo, Madrid, and Chicago. Try as we might on long winter evenings to tune the needle in and hear a play in Japanese or Russian, all we ever got was CHMJ Moose Jaw, The Buckle of the Wheat Belt. Even so, I spent hours lying on the floor, tracing the floral patterns on the front of the speaker while I listened to another world of mystery and fascination.

When the time came that Grandad could find no more work, he set a kitchen chair in front of the radio and stayed there, not moving except to go to the King William with Uncle Fred. My Dad managed to get a job with the city, gravelling streets for forty cents a day. But things grew worse. The Moose Jaw Light and Power Company came around one day in the fall of 1937 and cut off our electricity for non-payment. It was hard on Grandad not to have his radio. Not only did he have nothing to do, but he had to spend all his time thinking about it. So he stared out the parlour window, which looked over the alley behind the hardware store. There was a view of the rear of the Rainbow Laundry, probably the dreariest vista in town.

That was what he was doing the day of his discovery, just before Christmas. Uncle Fred and my Dad were arguing about who had caused the Depression — R.B. Bennett or the C.P.R. Suddenly Grandad turned from the window. There was a new and strange look on his face. "Where does that wire go?" he said.

"Wire?" said Uncle Fred, looking absent-mindedly around the room. He patted his pockets looking for a wire.

"What wire?" my Dad said.

Grandad nodded toward the window. "This wire running right past the window." He pointed to a double strand of power line that ran from a pole in the back alley to the side of our building. It was a lead-in for the hardware store below.

"Holy Moses Cousin Harry. Isn't that a sight now!" Grandad said, grinning crazily.

"You're nuts!" Uncle Fred told him. "You'll never get a tap off that line there. They'd find you out in nothing flat."

Grandma, who always heard everything that was said, called from the kitchen: "Father, don't you go and do some foolishness will have us all electrinated."

"By Jayzuz," he muttered. He never paid attention to anything she said. "Cut off *my* power, will they?"

That night, after I went to bed, I listened to him and Uncle Fred banging and scraping as they bored a hole through the parlour wall. My Dad wouldn't have anything to do with it and took my mother to the free movie at the co-op. He said Grandad was descending to the level of the Moose Jaw Light and Power Company.

As it happened, Grandad was an experienced electrician. He had known for a long time how to jump a wire from one side of the meter to the other, to cheat the power company. I had often watched him under the meter, stretched out on tiptoe at the top of a broken stepladder, yelling at Grandma to lift the God-damned Holy Candle *higher* so he could see what the Christ he was doing.

The next day, Grandad and Uncle Fred were acting like a couple of kids, snorting and giggling and jabbing each other in the ribs. They were eager for the King William beer parlour to open so they could go and tell their friends about Grandad's revenge on the power company. There they spent the day like heroes, telling over and over how Grandad had spied the lead-in, and how they had bored the hole through the wall, and how justice had finally descended on the capitalist leeches. They came home for supper, but as soon as they ate they headed back to the King William. Everybody was buying them free beer.

Grandma didn't think much of their efforts, though she claimed to enjoy the benefits of electrical power. The line came through the hole in the wall, across the parlour floor to the kitchen and the hall. Other cords were attached which led to the two bedrooms. Grandma muttered in irritation when she had to sweep around the black tangle of wires and sockets. She had that quaint old-country belief that electricity leaked from every connection and with six of us living in the tiny suite, somebody was forever tripping on one of the cords and knocking things over.

But we lived with all that because Grandad was happy again. We might *all* have lived happily if Grandad and Uncle Fred could have kept silent about their revenge on the power company.

One night about a week later we were in the parlour listening to Fibber McGee and Molly when somebody knocked at the door. It was Mrs. Pizak, who lived next door in a tiny room.

''Goot evening,'' she said, looking all around. ''I see your power has turnt beck on.''

''Ha,'' Grandad said. ''We turned it on *for* 'em. Damned rogues.''

''Come in and listen to the show with us,'' Grandma said. Mrs. Pizak kept looking at the black wires running back and forth across the parlour, and at Grandad's radio. You could tell she wasn't listening to the show.

''Dey shut off my power, too,'' she said. ''I alvays like listen de Shut-In program. Now my radio isn't vork.''

''Hmmm,'' Grandad said, trying to hear Fibber and the Old-Timer. Grandma and my Dad watched him, not listening to the radio any more either. Finally he couldn't stand it.

''All right, Fred,'' he said. ''Go and get the brace and bit.''

They bored a hole through one of the bedroom walls into Mrs. Pizak's cubicle, and she was on Grandad's power grid, too. It didn't take long for everybody else in the block to find out about the free power. They all wanted to hook up. There were two floors of apartments above the hardware store, and soon the walls and ceiling of Grandad's suite were as full of holes as a colander, with wires running in all directions. For the price of a bottle of whiskey, people could run their lights twenty-four hours a day if they wanted. By Christmas Day, even those neighbours who *paid* their bills had given notice to the power company. It was a tolerable Christmas in a bad year — and Grandad and Uncle Fred liked to take credit for it. Which everyone gave them. There was a lot of celebration up and down the halls, where they always showed up as guests of honour. A funny feeling ran through the block, like being in a state of siege, or a revolution, with Grandad and Uncle Fred leading it.

One late afternoon just before New Year's, I was lying on the parlour floor, reading a second-hand Book of Knowledge I had gotten for Christmas. Grandma and my mother were knitting socks, and all three of us were half-listening to Major Bowes' amateur show. From the corner of my eye, I thought I saw Grandad's radio move. I blinked and stared at it, but the big console just sat there quoting the Major's tactful enthusiasm. I turned a page. Again, it seemed to move in a jerk.

"Grandma," I said. "The radio —"

She looked up from her knitting, already not believing a word I might have to say. I gave up and glared at the offending machine. While I watched, it slid at least six inches across the parlour floor.

"Grandma!" I screamed. "The radio's moving! All by itself!"

She looked calmly at the radio, then the tangle of wires spread across the floor, and then out the parlour window.

"Larry-boy, you'd best run and fetch your grandfather. He's over at McBrides'."

McBrides' suite was along the gloomy hall a few doors. I sprinted the whole distance and pounded frantically at the door. Someone opened it the width of a crack. "Is my Grandad in there?" I squeaked.

Grandad stepped out into the hall with a glass in his hand, closing the door behind him. "What is it, Larry?"

"Grandma says you to come quick. There's something wrong with the radio!"

"My radio!" Like most small men, he had the energy of a race-horse. He started walking back up the hall, broke into a trot, then a steady gallop, holding his glass of whiskey out in front at arms length so it wouldn't spill. He burst through the door and skidded to a stop in front of the radio, which sat there, perfectly normal except that it stood maybe a foot to the left of his chair.

"By the Holy Toenails of Moses — what is it?"

Grandma looked up and jerked her chin ominously toward the window. Her quiet firmness usually managed to calm him, but now, in two fantastic bounds, Grandad stood glaring out the window.

"Larry," he said, turning to me with a pale face, "fetch your Uncle Fred." I tore off down the hall again to number eight and fetched Uncle Fred. When he entered the suite, the two women were still knitting. Grandma was doing her stitches calmly enough, but my mother's needles clattered like telegraph keys, and she was throwing terrified glances around the room.

Grandad had not moved. "Have a gawk at *this*, will you, Fred."

Uncle Fred and I crowded around him to see out. There, on a pole only twenty feet from our parlour window, practically facing us eye-to-eye, was a lineman from the power company. He was replacing broken glass insulators; God knows why he was doing it in the dead of winter. He could not have noticed our home-made lead-in, or he would have been knocking at our door. We could only pray he wouldn't look at the wire too closely. Once, he lifted his eyes toward the lighted window where we stood gaping out at him in the growing darkness. He grinned at us, and raised his hand in a salute. He must have thought we were admiring his work.

"Wave back!" Grandad ordered. The three of us waved frantically at the lineman, to make him think we appreciated his efforts, although Grandad was muttering some very ugly things about the man's ancestry.

Finally, to our relief, the lineman finished his work and got ready to come down the pole. He reached out his hand for support — and my heart stopped beating as his weight hung on the contraband wire. Behind me, I could hear the radio slide another foot across the parlour floor. The lineman stared at the wire he held. He tugged experimentally, his eyes following it up to the hole through our wall. He looked at Grandad and Uncle Fred and me standing there in the lit-up window, with our crazy horror-struck grins and our arms frozen above our heads in grotesque waves. Understanding spread slowly across his face.

He scrambled around to the opposite side of the pole and braced himself to give a mighty pull on our line. Simultaneously, Grandad leaped into action, grabbing the wire on our side of the wall. He wrapped it around his hands, and braced his feet against the baseboard. The lineman gave his first vicious yank, and it almost jerked Grandad smack against the wall. I remember thinking what a powerful man the lineman must be to do that to my Grandad.

''Fred, you feather-brained idiot!'' he shouted. ''Get over here and *haul* before the black-hearted son of a bitch pulls me through the wall.''

Uncle Fred ran to the wire just in time, as the man on the pole gave another, mightier heave. From the window, I could see him stiffen with rage and determination. The slender wire sawed back and forth through the hole in the wall for at least ten minutes, first one side, then the other, getting advantage. The curses on our side got very loud and bitter. I couldn't hear the lineman, but I could see him — with his mouth twisted in an awful snarl, throwing absolutely terrible looks at me in the window, and heaving on the line. He was not praying to St Jude.

Grandad's cursing would subside periodically when Grandma warned: ''Now, now, father, not in front of the boy.'' Then she would go back to her knitting and pretend the whole affair wasn't happening, and Grandad's blasphemies would soar to monumental heights.

That lineman must have been in extra-good condition, because our side quickly began to play out. Grandad yelled at Grandma and my mother, even at me, to throw ourselves on the line and help. But the women refused to leave their knitting, and they would not allow me to be corrupted. I didn't want to leave my viewpoint at the window, anyway.

Grandad and Uncle Fred kept losing footage until the huge radio had scraped all the way across the floor and stood at their backs, hampering their efforts.

''Larry!'' Grandad shouted. ''Is he weakenin' any?''

He wanted desperately for me to say yes, but it was useless. ''It doesn't look like it,'' I said. Grandad burst out in a froth of curses I'd never heard before. A fresh attack on the line pulled his knuckles to the wall and barked them badly. He looked tired and beaten. All the slack in the line was taken up. He was against the wall, his head twisted, looking at me. A light flared in his eyes.

''All right, Fred,'' he said. ''If he wants the God-damned thing so bad — let him have it!'' They both jumped back — and nothing happened.

I could see the lineman, completely unaware of his impending disaster, literally winding himself up for an all-out assault on our wire. I wanted, out of human kindness, to shout a warning at him. But it was too late. With an incredible backward lunge, he disappeared from sight behind the power pole.

A shattering explosion of wild noises blasted around us, like a bomb had fallen in Grandad's suite. Every electric appliance and light that Grandma owned flew into the parlour, bounding off the walls and smashing against each other. A table lamp from the bedroom caromed off Uncle Fred's knee. A radio collided against the wall and was ripped off its wire. Sparking and flashing like lightning, all of Grandma's things hurled themselves against the parlour walls, popping like a string of firecrackers as the cords went zipping through the hole. A silence fell — like a breath of air to a drowning man. The late afternoon darkness settled through the room.

"Sweet Jesus Christ!" Grandad said. Then there came a second uproar: a blood-curdling series of roars and shouting, as all our neighbours recovered from seeing their lamps, radios, irons, and toasters leap from their tables and collect in ruined piles of junk around the "free power" holes in their walls. Uncle Fred turned white as a sheet.

I looked out the window. The lineman sat at the foot of his pole, dazed. He looked up at me with one more hate-filled glare, then deliberately snipped our wire with a pair of cutters, taped the end and marched away into the night.

Grandad stood in the midst of the total darkness and the ruins of his home, trying to examine his beloved radio for damage. Grandma sat in her rocking chair, knitting socks and refusing to acknowledge the adventure.

It was Grandad who finally broke the silence. "Well! They're lucky," he said. "It's just damned lucky for them they didn't scratch my radio!"

Willi

E. L. Doctorow

E. L. Doctorow

(United States, b. 1931)

E. L. Doctorow's *Lives of the Poets*, the book from which "Willi" is taken, appears to be a collection of seven unrelated short stories. In fact, the title novella reveals that the six other pieces are the imaginings of a certain writer who, from his Soho apartment, dreams of the world he knows and the worlds he has created — like Hemingway's dying novelist in *The Snows of Kilimanjaro*. Christopher Lehmann-Haupt, reviewing one of Doctorow's most successful novels, *Ragtime*, asked, "Why do its images seem truer than the truth?" Perhaps because Doctorow's selective eye rearranges the known facts so as to reveal their true nature, unencumbered by chronological or geographical considerations. In "Willi," for instance, only a master's hand would have been wise enough to place the last line of the story where it now stands, suddenly shifting the reader's perspective to a more merciful — and more understanding — point of view.

Willi

I walked in the meadow behind the barn and felt rising around me the exhalations of the field, the moist sweetness of the grasses, and I imagined the earth's soul lifting to the warmth of the sun and mingling me in some divine embrace. There was such brilliant conviction in the colors of the golden hay meadow, the blue sky, that I could not help laughing. I threw myself down in the grass and spread my arms. I fell at once into a trance and yet remained incredibly aware, so that whatever I opened my eyes to look at I did not merely see but felt as its existence. Such states come naturally to children. I was resonant with the hum of the universe, I was made indistinguishable from the world in a great bonding of natural revelation. I saw the drowse of gnats weaving between the grasses and leaving infinitesimally fine threads of shimmering net, so highly textured that the breath of the soil below lifted it in gentle billows. Minute crawling life on the stalks of hay made colossal odyssey, journeys of a lifetime, before my eyes. Yet there was no thought of miracle, of the miracle of microscopic sentience. The scale of the universe was not pertinent, and the smallest indications of energy were in proportion to the sun, which lay like an Egyptian eye between the stalks, and lit them as it lights the earth, by halves. The hay had fallen under me so that my own body's outline was patterned on the field, the outspread legs and arms, the fingers, and I was aware of my being as the arbitrary shape of an agency that had chosen to make me in this manner as a means of communicating with me. The very idea of a head and limbs and a body was substantive only as an act of communication, and I felt myself in the prickle of the flattened grass, and the sense of imposition was now enormous, a prodding, a lifting of this part of the world that was for some reason my momentary responsibility, that was giving me possession of itself. And I rose and seemed to ride on the planes of the sun, which I felt in fine striations, alternated with thin lines of the earth's moist essences. And invisibled by my revelation, I reached the barn and examined the face of it, standing with my face in the painted whiteness of its glare as a dog or a cat stands nose to a door until someone comes and lets it out. And I moved along the white barn wall, sidestepping until I came to the window which was a simple square without glass, and could only be felt by the geometrical coolness of its volume of inner air, for it was black within. And there I stood, as if in the mouth of a vacuum, and felt the insubstantial being of the sun meadow pulled past me into the barn, like a torrential implosion of light into darkness and life into death, and I myself too disintegrated in that force and was sucked like the chaff of the field in that roaring. Yet I stood where I was. And in quite normal spatial relationship with my surroundings felt the sun's quiet warmth on my back and the coolness of the cool barn on my face. And the windy universal roar in my ears had narrowed and refined itself to a recognizable frequency, that of a woman's pulsating song in the act of love, the gasp and note and gasp and note of an ecstatic score. I listened. And pressed upon by the sun, as if it were a hand on the back of my neck, I moved my face into the portal of the cool darkness, and no longer blinded by the sunlight, my eyes saw on the straw and in the dung my mother, denuded, in a pose of utmost degradation, a body, a reddened headless body, the head enshrouded in her clothing, everything turned inside out, as if blown out by the wind, all order, truth, and reason, and this defiled mama played violently upon and being made to sing her defilement. How can I describe what I felt! I felt I deserved to see this! I felt it was my triumph, but I felt monstrously betrayed. I felt drained suddenly of the strength to stand. I turned my back and slid down the wall to a sitting position under the window. My heart in my chest banged in sickened measure of her cries. I wanted to kill him, this killer of my mother who was killing her. I wanted to leap through the window and drive a pitchfork into his back, but I wanted him to be killing her, I wanted him to be killing her for me. I wanted to be him. I lay on the ground, and with my arms over my head and my hands clasped and my ankles locked, I rolled down the slope behind the barn, through the grass and the crop of hay. I flattened the hay like a mechanical cylinder of irrepressible force rolling fast and faster over rocks, through rivulets, across furrows and over hummocks of the uneven imperfect flawed irregular earth, the sun flashing in my closed eyes in diurnal emergency, as if time and the planet had gone out of control. As it has. (I am recalling these things now, a man older than my father when he died, and to whom a woman of my mother's age when all this happened is a young woman barely half my age. What an incredible achievement of fantasy is the scientific mind! We posit an empirical world, yet how can I be here at this desk in this room — and not be here? If memory is a matter of the stimulation of so many cells of the brain, the greater the stimulus — remorse, the recognition of fate — the more powerfully complete becomes the sensation of the memory until there is transfer, as in a time machine, and the memory is in the ontological sense another reality.) Papa, I see you now in the universe of your own making. I walk the polished floorboards of your house and seat myself at your dining table. I feel the tassels of the tablecloth on the tops of my bare knees. The light of the candelabra shines on your smiling mouth of big teeth. I notice the bulge of your neck produced by your shirt collar. Your pink scalp is visible through the close-cropped German-style haircut. I see your head raised in conversation and your white plump hand of consummate gesture making its point to your wife at the other end of the table. Mama is so attentive. The candle flame burns in her eyes and I imagine the fever there, but she is quite calm and seriously engrossed by what you say. Her long neck, very white, is hung with a thin chain from which depends on the darkness of her modest dress a cream-coloured cameo, the carved profile of another fine lady of another time. In her neck a soft slow pulse beats. Her small hands are folded and the bones of her wrists emerge from the touch of lace at her cuffs. She is smiling at you in your loving proprietorship, proud of you, pleased to be yours, and the mistress of this house, and the mother of this boy. Of my tutor across the table from me who idly twirls the stem of his wine-glass and glances at her, she is barely aware. Her eyes are for her husband. I think now Papa her feelings in this moment are sincere. I know now each moment has its belief and what we call treachery is the belief of each moment, the wish for it to be as it seems to be. It is possible in joy to love the person you have betrayed and to be refreshed in your love for him, it is entirely possible. Love renews all faces and customs and ideals and leaves the bars of the prison shining. But how could a boy know that? I ran to my room and waited for someone to follow me. Whoever dared to enter my room, I would attack — would pummel. I wanted it to be her, I wanted her to come to me, to hug me and to hold my head and kiss me on the lips as she liked to do, I wanted her to make those wordless sounds of comfort as she held me to her when I was hurt or unhappy, and when she did that I would beat her with my fists, beat her to the floor, and see her raise her hands helplessly in terror as I beat her and kicked her and jumped upon her and drove the breath from her body. But it was my tutor who, sometime later, opened the door, looked in with his hand upon the knob, smiled, said a few words, and wished me good night. He closed the door and I heard him walk up the steps to the next floor, where he had his rooms. Ledig was his name. He was a Christian. I had looked but could not find in his face any sign of smugness or leering pride or cruelty. There was nothing coarse about him, nothing that could possibly give me offense. He was barely twenty. I even thought I saw in his eyes a measure of torment. He was habitually melancholic anyway, and during my lessons his mind often wandered and he would gaze out the window and sigh. He was as much a schoolboy as his pupil. So there was every reason to refrain from judgment, to let time pass, to think, to gain understanding. Nobody knew that I knew. I had that choice. But did I? They had made my position intolerable. I was given double vision, the kind that comes with a terrible blow. I found I could not have anything to do with my kind sweet considerate mother. I found I could not bear the gentle pedagogics of my tutor. How, in that rural isolation, could I be expected to go on? I had no friends, I was not permitted to play with the children of the peasants who worked for us. I had only this trinity of Mother and Tutor and Father, this unholy trinity of deception and ignorance who had excommunicated me from my life at the age of thirteen. This of course in the calendar of traditional Judaism is the year a boy enjoys his initiation into manhood.

Meanwhile my father was going about the triumph of his life, running a farm according to the most modern principles of scientific management, astonishing his peasants and angering the other farmers in the region with his success. The sun brought up his crops, the Galician Agricultural Society gave him an award for the quality of his milk, and he lived in the state of abiding satisfaction given to individuals who are more than a match for the life they have chosen for themselves. I had incorporated him into the universe of giant powers that I, a boy, experienced in the changes of the seasons. I watched bulls bred to cows, watched mares foal, I saw life come from the egg and the multiplicative wonders of mudholes and ponds, the jell and slime of life shimmering in gravid expectation. Everywhere I looked, life sprang from something not life, insects unfolded from sacs on the surface of still waters and were instantly on the prowl for their dinner, everything that came into being knew at once what to do and did it unastonished that it was what it was, unimpressed by where it was, the great earth heaving up its bloodied newborns from every pore, every cell, bearing the variousness of itself from every conceivable substance which it contained in itself, sprouting life that flew or waved in the wind or blew from the mountains or stuck to the damp black underside of rocks, or swam or suckled or bellowed or silently separated in two. I placed my father in all of this as the owner and manager. He lived in the universe of giant powers by understanding it and making it serve him, using the daily sun for his crops and breeding what naturally bred, and so I distinguished him in it as the god-eye in the kingdom, the intelligence that brought order and gave everything its value. He loved me and I can still feel my pleasure in making him laugh, and I might not be deceiving myself when I remember the feel on my infant hand of his unshaved cheek, the winy smell of his breath, the tobacco smoke in his thick wavy hair, or his mock-wondering look of foolish happiness during our play together. He had close-set eyes, the color of dark grapes, that opened wide in our games. He would laugh like a horse and show large white teeth. He was a strong man, stocky and powerful — the constitution I inherited — and he had emerged as an orphan from the alleys of cosmopolitan eastern Europe, like Darwin's amphibians from the sea, and made himself a landowner, a husband and father. He was a Jew who spoke no Yiddish and a farmer raised in the city. I was not allowed to play with village children, or to go to their crude schools. We lived alone, isolated on our estate, neither Jew nor Christian, neither friend nor petitioner of the Austro-Hungarians, but in the pride of the self-constructed self. To this day I don't know how he arranged it or what hungering rage had caused him to deny every classification society imposes and to live as an anomaly, tied to no past in a world which, as it happened, had no future. But I am in awe that he did it. Because he stood up in his life he was exposed to the swords of Mongol horsemen, the scythes of peasants in revolution, the lowered brows of monstrous bankers and the cruciform gestures of prelates. His arrogance threatened him with the cumulative power of all of European history which was ready to take his head, nail it to a pole and turn him into one of the scarecrows in his fields, arms held stiffly out toward life. But when the moment came for this transformation, it was accomplished quite easily, by a word from his son. I was the agency of his downfall. Ancestry and myth, culture, history and time were ironically composed in the shape of his own boy.

I watched her for several days. I remembered the rash of passion on her flesh. I was so ashamed of myself that I felt continuously ill, and it was the vaguest, most diffuse nausea, nausea of the blood, nausea of the bone. In bed at night I found it difficult breathing, and terrible waves of fever broke over me and left me parched in my terror. I couldn't purge from my mind the image of her overthrown body, the broad whitenesses, her shoed feet in the air; I made her scream ecstatically every night in my dreams and awoke one dawn in my own sap. That was the crisis that toppled me, for in fear of being found out by the maid and by my mother, for fear of being found out by them all as the archcriminal of my dreams, I ran to him, I went to him for absolution, I confessed and put myself at his mercy. Papa, I said. He was down by the kennels mating a pair of vizslas. He used this breed to hunt. He had rigged some sort of harness for the bitch so that she could not bolt, a kind of pillory, and she was putting up a terrible howl, and though her tail showed her amenable, she moved her rump away from the proddings of the erect male, who mounted and pumped and missed and mounted again and couldn't hold her still. My father was banging the fist of his right hand into the palm of his left. Put it to her, he shouted, come on, get it in there, give it to her. Then the male had success and the mating began, the female standing there quietly now, sweat dripping off her chops, an occasional groan escaping from her. And then the male came, and stood front paws on her back, his tongue lolling as he panted, and they waited as dogs do for the detumescence. My father knelt beside them and soothed them with quiet words. Good dogs, he said, good dogs. You must guard them at this time, he said to me, they try to uncouple too early and hurt themselves. Papa, I said. He turned and looked at me over his shoulder as he knelt beside the dogs, and I saw his happiness, and the glory of him in his work-pants tucked into a black pair of riding boots and his shirt open at the collar and the black hair of his chest curled as high as the throat, and I said, Papa, they should be named Mama and Ledig. And then I turned so quickly I do not even remember his face changing, I did not even wait to see if he understood me, I turned and ran, but I am sure of this — he never called after me.

There was a sun room in our house, a kind of conservatory with a glass outer wall and slanted ceiling of green glass framed in steel. It was a very luxurious appointment in that region, and it was my mother's favorite place to be. She had filled it with plants and books, and she liked to lie on a chaise in this room and read and smoke cigarettes. I found her there, as I knew I would, and I glazed at her with wonder and fascination because I knew her fate. She was incredibly beautiful, with her dark hair parted in the center and tied behind her in a bun, and her small hands, and the lovely fullness of her chin, the indications under her chin of some fattening, like a quality of indolence in her character. But a man would not dwell on this as on her neck, so lovely and slim, or the high modestly dressed bosom. A man would not want to see signs of the future. Since she was my mother it had never occurred to me how many years younger she was than my father. He had married her out of the gymnasium; she was the eldest of four daughters and her parents had been eager to settle her in prosperous welfare, which is what a mature man offers. It is not that the parents are unaware of the erotic component for the man in this sort of marriage. They are fully aware of it. Rectitude, propriety, are always very practical. I gazed at her in wonder and awe. I blushed. What? she said. She put her book down and smiled and held out her arms. What, Willi, what is it? I fell into her arms and began to sob as she held me and my tears wet the dark dress she wore. She held my head and whispered, What, Willi, what did you do to yourself, poor Willi? Then, aware that my sobs had become breathless and hysterical, she held me at arm's length — tears and snot were dribbling from me — and her eyes widened in genuine alarm.

That night I heard from the bedroom the shocking exciting sounds of her undoing. I have heard such terrible sounds of blows upon a body in Berlin after the war, Freikorps hoodlums in the streets attacking whores they had dragged from the brothel and tearing the clothes from their bodies and beating them to the cobblestones. I sat up in bed, hardly able to breathe, terrified, but feeling undeniable arousal. Give it to her, I muttered, banging my fist in my palm. Give it to her. But then I could bear it no longer and ran into their room and stood between them, lifting my screaming mother from the bed, holding her in my arms, shouting at my father to stop, to stop. But he reached around me and grabbed her hair with one hand and punched her face with the other. I was enraged, I pushed her back and jumped at him, pummeling him, shouting that I would kill him. This was in Galicia in the year 1910. All of it was to be destroyed anyway, even without me.

Uncle Facundo

Isidoro Blaisten

Isidoro Blaisten

(Argentina, b. 1933)

In 1967 I got my first job at an Argentine publishing company that had a staff of two. I quickly became the third most important person in the company. We needed good manuscripts, and it occurred to me that if we asked established writers whether they knew of any promising young talents, we might end up with a few publishable books. It worked: Jorge Luis Borges recommended Vlady Kociancich, an excellent short-story writer and novelist, and Marta Lynch, one of the most popular novelists in Spanish, suggested the name of Isidoro Blaisten. Blaisten was working as a bookseller in downtown Buenos Aires, in a small musty shop where even the new books came out of their cartons covered in fine dust. He had been writing short stories for several years, and with some reluctance left 300 pages in our office. The manuscript turned out to be a hilarious, wonderfully written collection that seemed to fit no given trend or tradition. Blaisten let himself write with no fixed purpose, and his reality would acquire shapes totally credible and yet impossible. Blaisten's first book was called *Happiness*, the second *South of Dublin*. "Uncle Facundo" is the first of his stories to be translated into English.

Uncle Facundo

Just so that you can see what my family was really like before we decided to kill off Uncle Facundo — I mean, before Uncle Facundo arrived — let me tell you what each of us used to say.

Mother would say:

Dogs can always tell when their master is about to die, there's nothing worse than having an operation when you're running a fever, penicillin gobbles up your red corpuscles, she'd say, children dehydrate in summer, she'd say, boys are usually on their mother's side and girls on their father's, she'd say, children of split marriages are always sad, she'd say, Jewish doctors are the best, she'd say, mothers always love the wicked sons more, she'd say, those who have the most are those who spend the least, and some poor soul . . . she'd say, to think he walked around with that cancer inside him, she'd say, wallpaper collects bugs, she'd say, in the old days people used to die of the flu.

Father would say:

Swimming is the only real sport, the Germans lost the war in Russia because of the cold, soldiers and sailors have unfaithful wives, and travelling salesmen as well, nothing shaves as close as an old-fashioned razor, a good glass of red wine is great in the winter, beer in the summer, thin women are really hot, red wine should never be drunk cold, black tobacco is healthier than blond tobacco, no doctor operates on his own wife, all that the workers want is one hot meal a day, they go begging in the streets and have a savings account in the bank, thieves should have their hands chopped off and be hung in the public square, the best fertilizer is horse shit, the only money is in farming, barbecues should be eaten standing up, countryfolk have no problems, a few potatoes, a couple of eggs, kill a chicken and that's that.

My sister would say:

There's nothing nicer than going to the movies when it's raining. A lonely bird will die of a broken heart. Blond people go red in the sun, dark people don't. They go from man to man and then. I hate films that make you cry. I adore studying and learning and studying and —. I won't be like those who get married in white.

I would say:

You really have to take your hat off to the German economy. All Japanese are traitors. Swimming softens your muscles. Grumpy people get over their anger very quickly. No steady girlfriends till I get my degree. I want to study. No politics in class.

This is what my family was like until Uncle Facundo arrived. Father worked at the railroad, Traffic Bureau, Retiro Terminal. He would get up at five in the morning, sip his *maté* while reading the paper from beginning to end, and then walk the seven blocks to Saavedra Station. Mother looked after the house, watered the plants and watched television. My sister did decorative wood-burning, had a job as a teacher and studied to be a social worker.

I was studying economics and working as an accountant's assistant at Bonplart Textiles.

I remember that when we were kids, my mother and father would talk about Uncle Facundo in whispers. When I or my sister came near, they would interrupt their conversation.

On summer nights father would bring out the wicker chair for mother, the low stool for himself, the Viennese chair, which I used to turn round, for me, and the deck chair for my sister.

On those nights it always happened that when father, after commenting on the state of the backyard wall, would tell us again about how they had published his letter to the editor, mother — I don't know why — would talk about Uncle Facundo.

Uncle Facundo was mother's brother, and also the brother of Aunt Fermina. Neither father nor I or my sister had ever met him. When mother got engaged to father, Uncle Facundo had already disappeared. When we were old enough to understand, mother told us that Uncle Facundo had got married in a town called Casilda and that his wife had died under mysterious circumstances. Evil gossip and Aunt Fermina said that Uncle Facundo had done away with her.

Uncle Facundo was the black sheep in mother's family. Aunt Fermina said that she no longer thought of him as her brother and that his behaviour had sent grandma to an early grave.

One day we received the following telegram from Uncle Facundo:

> Dear brothers, sisters, nephews and nieces:
> Arriving Friday 10. International train, Posadas.

Father was against allowing him into the house but mother said that in spite of everything he was her brother, and that the poor boy must be feeling very lonely, and that if he had chosen our home instead of Aunt Fermina's, there was probably a good reason.

So on Friday 10 at a quarter to midnight, we all sat expectantly in Chacarita Station. The train was almost two hours late and while we waited in the restaurant we fell into an argument.

Father said that Uncle Facundo was a bum, and that if he

wanted to stay for a few days with us, fine, but that he shouldn't imagine that father was going to keep him for the rest of his life. Mother and my sister said that as soon as a man is driven to the edge, someone will step on his fingers rather than come to the rescue. I said nothing. Then the train arrived.

We had difficulty finding Uncle Facundo. The only one who knew him was mother, so we just stared into her face. At last she saw him.

He was standing against a column, clutching a parcel that looked like a large shoe box.

And then, as I stared at him, I had the impression that I had always known him — all my life. Uncle Facundo gave everyone that impression. And when we were next to him, he lifted mother into the air and kissed her, hugged father till he made him cough, took Angelita in his arms as if she were his bride, and me, he just put a hand on my shoulder without saying anything, a conniving sparkling look in his eyes.

"Come on, let's have a drink!" he shouted. "I want to show you a few things."

Father said that first we should get the luggage. But Uncle Facundo had brought no luggage — only the shoe box.

In the restaurant he ordered white wine for everyone. Mother and father glanced at each other. With the exception of father (just a little with lots of water) no one at home drinks at all. But my sister, who seemed to be walking on thin air, desperately wanted to see what Uncle Facundo had brought for her. The truth is, we were all very much intrigued, and we gulped down the wine and even had a second round. Mother seemed transformed, laughing out loud like mad, especially when Uncle Facundo lifted the lid off the box and placed in her hands a Paraguayan shawl knitted in *ñanduti* lace by the Indians. It was beautiful, done in wonderful colours. It was something mother had longed for all her life.

And that night Uncle Facundo charmed us all. We each got things which we had always longed for. Father received a box of Havana cigars. Havanas from Havana. The best, the most expensive, not the stinking cheroots Michelini brings him from Brazil. Havanas.

He gave my sister a ring and a matching necklace. The links fitted one inside the other, growing or diminishing in size, and when they all came together you could see an aquamarine hanging between the gold and silver. My sister jumped up and kissed him.

When he gave me the penknife I think I felt faint. It was a Solingen blade, with a silver handle inlaid with gold, wrought with the finest craftsmanship I have ever seen, either before or since.

We had another round of drinks. Father paid and we drove home in a taxi. And that night no one, except Uncle Facundo, managed to sleep.

That was the first battle Uncle Facundo won against us. Sometimes I think, what good did it do him? But I also wonder what good did it do us to have killed him. What good did it do mother to have smothered him with a pillow, father to have strangled him, myself to have dug the little penknife between his sternum and the main arteries, while my sister cut his veins with a disposable razor blade?

What good did it all do us, I wonder, if Uncle Facundo is still there, embedded in the backyard soil, sideways, like a swimmer, shrunk perhaps, or perhaps leaving nothing but a hollow shape there where his flesh once was, while the cement continues to bake in the sun, and Uncle Facundo's spirit haunts the wall. . . . But all that was later, much later, when we had no choice but to kill him.

On the day after that memorable night, Uncle Facundo was the first to get out of bed. And this also became a memorable event, because in all the time he stayed with us, up to the very day of his death (and especially on that day) it was necessary to shake him for hours to wake him.

It was a Saturday. Uncle Facundo went into the backyard and, next to the wall that was to be his tomb, found a few empty tar tins, and a bunch of tools. With those he built mother a kind of shelving for the den, and then went inside to wake her up with a *maté*.

At midday, when we all got up and saw what Uncle Facundo had done, we expressed admiration for his handicraft; and I remember he said that real work was the work done with the hands, and that all the rest, papers and numbers, were a charade and chicken-shit.

Lunch was like a party. Uncle Facundo told us all about the time he had harvested rice in Entre Rios and stories about the ranches he had worked on in Corrientes. But the funniest part was when he told us what he had done when he had worked as a gravedigger in Casilda. At that point, he sent my sister out to buy two more bottles of wine. Mother, her eyes gleaming, suggested a game of bingo, but Uncle Facundo said poker was better, and we all looked at each other because none of us knew how to play and we only had a pack of Spanish cards.

Mother asked what poker cards looked like. Uncle Facundo told her, and mother rummaged around in the closet and appeared with an unopened box that had a set of dominoes, a top, two packs of French cards and plastic chips, which she had bought on sale at Gath & Chaves. "Are these the right ones?" she asked, taking off the cellophane wrapping. Luckily they were, and Uncle Facundo taught us to play. Poker turned out to be the most wonderful, prodigious game we had ever played. At first the chips had no set value, but then we agreed they would be worth ten pesos each, and then fifty, and then a hundred, and father sent my sister for two more bottles of wine. Uncle Facundo called after her that two of rum would be even better. As Angelita was about to leave, Aunt Fermina appeared.

When Aunt Fermina saw what was lying on the table, she almost died. She didn't even bother to greet Uncle Facundo after so many years. She insulted him, called him names. Mother, who seemed a little drunk, spoke up for him. Father shook his head as in a daze, saying, "Peace, my dears, peace."

Suddenly father stood up and slapped my sister across the face from the other side of the table, scattering the chips and the money, and yelling at the top of his lungs: "So what are you waiting for, you idiot! Go get that bloody rum!"

It was the very first time I saw my father hit my sister.

Angelita ran away to the shops, and Uncle Facundo got up and went into the back yard, and stood by the wall, smoking, watching the stars that were beginning to come out.

Now that I think of it, it seems as if Uncle Facundo had a marked fondness for that wall in which he's now trapped, sideways and surrounded by bricks, the mouth and eyes full of cement. . . . Perhaps there's only air around the skeleton. . . . Well, you'd have to tap the wall to see.

In the end Aunt Fermina left, and at first no one seemed willing to eat a thing. But then Uncle Facundo started telling jokes, and sent my sister out for two more bottles, and taught mother how to cook *saltimboquis alla romana*, and we all had a royal banquet, drank the two bottles of rum and the wine, and went on playing poker till six in the morning.

Next morning the neighbours complained about the noise, and father, who skipped work for the first time in his life, almost hit Michelini.

And that's how it all began. Father and Uncle Facundo started going every Saturday and Sunday to the racetrack, and mother would give them her savings to bet on the horses.

Angelita brought home her girlfriends, also teachers, and Uncle Facundo taught them how to dance tango and then took them to bed with him. Mother was as happy as a lark and at night she'd go downtown with a young poet. Uncle Facundo approved wholeheartedly, saying it was healthy and part of life and that in life things had to be killed off by living them to the hilt, that beauty and sex should go hand in hand, and that people's real problem — when there were no wars to worry about — was that they were all bored out of their minds. That's why — he would say — neighbours stand at the door all day long living the life of others, that gossip was a form of frustrated romanticism, and that people gobbled up crime and pornography because they needed them, because they supplanted life, because real life was a whirlwind.

I brought over the guys from the university to hear him.

Up to there things could have worked out quite well. Father, who had always been someone incapable of harming a fly, had punched up almost every one of our neighbours. First they began by respecting him, then they became his followers and crowded along after father, admiring his paintings.

Father had discovered his ''hidden vocation,'' as Uncle Facundo called it, and his pictures now littered the house. Michelini used to come and stare at them for hours on end. Sometimes Michelini's eyes would cloud over, he'd pat father on the back, and leave without saying a word.

I had changed: I felt a new, personal magnetism. The girls in my class adored me and dropped by to see me at all hours.

We all felt alive. There was not a moment, not the slightest crack in time for us to wonder what to do. At night we danced, we played poker, we listened to Uncle Facundo; mother would read the young poet's latest stuff, father would paint, go over the racetrack papers, fight with the neighbours. We were alive.

But my sister began putting on the airs of a left-wing intellectual, and the ''political awareness'' bug bit her fiercely. First she started off with the ''stultification of the bourgeois sensibility,'' and then she carried on with the ''Catholic-Marxist dialogue.'' Father wanted to beat the shit out of her. So Angelita sided with Aunt Fermina.

Aunt Fermina spent her time chewing on her anger. Since Uncle Facundo had appeared she had tried once or twice to come to our house and preach at us, but she was afraid of father, who threatened to cut her throat every time he saw her. Now was her big chance.

The first thing Aunt Fermina did, helped by my sister, was creep into the house one Sunday morning while we were all asleep and, with the palette knife, rip father's paintings to shreds.

Poor father. He looked like the portrait of Dorian Gray. I

remember his face when he saw the slaughtered canvases, the empty tubes of paint, the trodden frames. He said nothing, not a word. But on Monday he was again as he had been before. He got up at five, sipped his *maté*, read the paper from one end to the other, and in the evening just sat outside the door, on the low stool, while we all danced indoors, played poker and listened to the young poet's poems.

And then father also became "aware of the facts." In no time at all he joined forces with my sister and Aunt Fermina. One thing is clear: even before Aunt Fermina took her next step, even before she convinced me (because mother was the last to give in, in spite of becoming the most vicious one of all — smothering Uncle Facundo with the pillow), even before father was won over by Aunt Fermina, something had to break, something that made things easy for Aunt Fermina. It was the sorry sight of father, walking around like a Martian, different, drifting among us, explaining to us how the Germans lost the war in Russia because of the cold, while those of us who remained on the side of Uncle Facundo continued to live on, regardless.

After that, it wasn't difficult for Aunt Fermina to win me over: I'm easy.

Life began to decline. But mother was as firm as a rock. She was the mistress of the young poet who, according to Uncle Facundo, saw in her both the ideal woman and a mother figure. The boy was crazy about mother and would write her the most wonderful verse. But mother was left on her own. And that's how Aunt Fermina achieved her goal. She grabbed hold of mother and put the question to her:

"You're the last one. Either we kill Facundo or we kill the poet."

Love triumphed. That night we decided to do away with Uncle Facundo. We found him asleep, an unforgettable smile on his lips. Father strangled him and I plunged my knife in between the sternum and the main arteries. My sister cut open his veins with a disposable razor blade. Aunt Fermina supervised everything.

We had trouble dragging mother away; she insisted on keeping the pillow pressed against his face.

Then we stood him up sideways and built another section of the wall around him. And that's all.

Now Uncle Facundo is there dead, inside that wall for ever, baking in the sun, and I can't stop looking at the wall with a certain sadness, especially on summer nights, when father brings out the wicker chair for mother, the low stool for himself, the Viennese chair, which I turn round, for me, and the deck chair for my sister, and mother says dogs can always tell when their master is about to die, and father says the only money is in farming, and my sister says a lonely bird will die of a broken heart, and I say all Japanese are traitors.

Translated from the Spanish by Alberto Manguel

Dayspring Mishandled

Rudyard Kipling

Rudyard Kipling
(India, 1865-1936)

For Rudyard Kipling, revenge took on the quality of a moral obligation. Man was supposed to fight back — against the injustices of his fellow men, of God, of nature. Revenge runs through Kipling's stories like a red thread, from Mowgli's revenge on the tiger, Shere Khan, in the *Jungle Books*, to the revenge of an English spinster on an innocent German soldier in ''Mary Postgate,'' one of Kipling's later stories. In most cases, however, revenge does not suit the avenger. In ''Dayspring Mishandled'' the revenge coils back again and again, trapping the characters in an inextricable tangle so intricate that its full meaning is revealed only to the very careful reader with an eye for detail. The details of his plot were of great concern to Kipling: he confessed to actually having forged a manuscript — paper, ink and text — in order to know exactly the mechanics he describes in this story. Kipling attributed his meticulous style to his miserable days as a child in Southsea. In his autobiography, he wrote that his unhappy childhood was not ''an unsuitable preparation for my future, in that it demanded a constant wariness, the habit of observation, and the attendance on moods and tempers; the noting of discrepancies between speech and action; a certain reserve of demeanour; and automatic suspicion of sudden favours.''

Dayspring Mishandled

C'est moi, c'est moi, c'est moi!
    Je suis la Mandragore!
La fille des beaux jours qui s'éveille à l'aurore —
    Et qui chante pour toi!

C. Nodier

In the days beyond compare and before the Judgements, a genius called Graydon foresaw that the advance of education and the standard of living would submerge all mind-marks in one mudrush of standardized reading matter, and so created the Fictional Supply Syndicate to meet the demand.

Since a few days' work for him brought them more money than a week's elsewhere, he drew many young men — some now eminent — into his employ. He bade them keep their eyes on the Sixpenny Dream Book, the Army and Navy Stores Catalogue (this for backgrounds and furniture as they changed), and *The Hearthstone Friend*, a weekly publication which specialized unrivalledly in the domestic emotions. Yet, even so, youth would not be denied, and some of the collaborated love-talk in "Passion Hath Peril," and "Ena's

Lost Lovers,'' and the account of the murder of the Earl in ''The Wickwire Tragedies'' — to name but a few masterpieces now never mentioned for fear of blackmail — was as good as anything to which their authors signed their real names in more distinguished years.

Among the young ravens driven to roost awhile on Graydon's ark was James Andrew Manallace — a darkish, slow northerner of the type that does not ignite, but must be detonated. Given written or verbal outlines of a plot, he was useless; but, with a half-dozen pictures round which to write his tale, he could astonish.

And he adored that woman who afterwards became the mother of Vidal Benzaquen, and who suffered and died because she loved one unworthy. There was also, among the company, a mannered, bellied person called Alured Castorley, who talked and wrote about ''Bohemia,'' but was always afraid of being ''compromised'' by the weekly suppers at Neminaka's Café in Hestern Square, where the Syndicate work was apportioned, and where everyone looked out for himself. He, too, for a time, had loved Vidal's mother, in his own way.

Now, one Saturday at Neminaka's, Graydon, who had given Manallace a sheaf of prints — torn from an extinct children's book called *Philippa's Queen* — on which to improvise, asked for results. Manallace went down into his ulster-pocket, hesitated a moment, and said the stuff had turned into poetry on his hands.

''Bosh!''

''That's what it isn't,'' the boy retorted. ''It's rather good.''

''Then it's no use to us.'' Graydon laughed. ''Have you brought back the cuts?''

Manallace handed them over. There was a castle in the series; a knight or so in armour; an old lady in a horned head-dress; a young ditto; a very obvious Hebrew; a clerk, with pen and inkhorn, checking wine barrels on a wharf; and a Crusader. On the back of one of the prints was a note, ''If he doesn't want to go, why can't he be captured and held to ransom?" Graydon asked what it all meant.

"I don't know yet. A comic opera, perhaps," said Manallace.

Graydon, who seldom wasted time, passed the cuts on to someone else, and advanced Manallace a couple of sovereigns to carry on with, as usual; at which Castorley was angry and would have said something unpleasant but was suppressed. Half-way through supper, Castorley told the company that a relative had died and left him an independence; and that he now withdrew from "hackwork" to follow "Literature." Generally, the Syndicate rejoiced in a comrade's good fortune, but Castorley had gifts of waking dislike. So the news was received with a vote of thanks, and he went out before the end, and, it was said, proposed to 'Dal Benzaquen's mother, who refused him. He did not come back. Manallace, who had arrived a little exalted, got so drunk before midnight that a man had to stay and see him home. But liquor never touched him above the belt, and when he had slept awhile, he recited to the gas-chandelier the poetry he had made out of the pictures; said that, on second thoughts, he would convert it into comic opera; deplored the Upas-tree influence of Gilbert and Sullivan; sang somewhat to illustrate his point; and — after words, by the way, with a negress in yellow satin — was steered to his rooms.

In the course of a few years, Graydon's foresight and genius were rewarded. The public began to read and reason upon higher planes, and the Syndicate grew rich. Later still, people demanded of their printed matter what they expected in their clothing and furniture. So, precisely as the three guinea handbag is followed in three weeks by its thirteen and sevenpence ha'penny, indistinguishable sister, they enjoyed perfect synthetic substitutes for Plot, Sentiment, and Emotion. Graydon died before the Cinema-caption school came in, but he left his widow twenty-seven thousand pounds.

Manallace made a reputation, and, more important, money for Vidal's mother when her husband ran away and the first symptoms of her paralysis showed. His line was the jocundly-sentimental Wardour Street brand of adventure, told in a style that exactly met, but never exceeded, every expectation.

As he once said when urged to "write a real book": "I've got my label, and I'm not going to chew it off. If you save people thinking, you can do anything with 'em." His output apart, he was genuinely a man of letters. He rented a small cottage in the country and economized on everything, except the care and charges of Vidal's mother.

Castorley flew higher. When his legacy freed him from "hackwork," he became first a critic — in which calling he loyally scalped all his old associates as they came up — and then looked for some speciality. Having found it (Chaucer was the prey), he consolidated his position before he occupied it, by his careful speech, his cultivated bearing, and the whispered words of his friends whom he, too, had saved the trouble of thinking. It followed that, when he published his first serious articles on Chaucer, all the world which is interested in Chaucer said: "This is an authority." But he was no impostor. He learned and knew his poet and his age; and in a month-long dog-fight in an austere literary weekly, met and mangled a recognized Chaucer expert of the day. He also, "for old sake's sake," as he wrote to a friend, went out of his way to review one of Manallace's books with an intimacy of unclean deduction (this was before the days of Freud) which long stood as a record. Some member of the extinct Syndicate took occasion to ask him if he would — for old sake's sake — help Vidal's mother to a new treatment. He answered that he had "known the lady very slightly and the calls on his purse were so heavy that," etc. The writer showed the letter to Manallace, who said he was glad Castorley hadn't interfered. Vidal's mother was then wholly paralysed. Only her eyes could move, and those always looked for the husband who had left her. She died thus in Manallace's arms in April of the first year of the War.

During the War he and Castorley worked as some sort of departmental dishwashers in the Office of Co-ordinated Supervisals. Here Manallace came to know Castorley again. Castorley, having a sweet tooth, cadged lumps of sugar for his tea from a typist, and when she took to giving them to a younger man, arranged that she should be reported for smoking in unauthorized apartments. Manallace possessed himself of every detail of the affair, as compensation for the review of his book. Then there came a night when, waiting for a big air-raid, the two men had talked humanly, and Manallace spoke of Vidal's mother. Castorley said something in reply, and from that hour — as was learned several years later — Manallace's real life-work and interests began.

The War over, Castorley set about to make himself Supreme Pontiff on Chaucer by methods not far removed from the employment of poison-gas. The English Pope was silent, through private griefs, and influenza had carried off the learned Hun who claimed continental allegiance. Thus Castorley crowed unchallenged from Upsala to Seville, while Manallace went back to his cottage with the photo of Vidal's mother over the mantelpiece. She seemed to have emptied out his life, and left him only fleeting interests in trifles. His private diversions were experiments of uncertain outcome, which, he said, rested him after a day's gadzooking and vitalstapping. I found him, for instance, one weekend, in his tool shed scullery, boiling a brew of slimy barks which were, if mixed with oak-galls, vitriol and wine, to become an ink-powder. We boiled it till the Monday, and it turned into an adhesive stronger than birdlime, and entangled us both.

At other times, he would carry me off, once in a few weeks, to sit at Castorley's feet, and hear him talk about Chaucer. Castorley's voice, bad enough in youth, when it could be shouted down, had, with culture and tact, grown almost insupportable. His mannerisms, too, had multiplied and set. He minced and mouthed, postured and chewed his words throughout those terrible evenings; and poisoned not only

Chaucer, but every shred of English literature which he used to embellish him. He was shameless, too, as regarded self-advertisement and ''recognition'' — weaving elaborate intrigues; forming petty friendships and confederacies, to be dissolved next week in favour of more promising alliances; fawning, snubbing, lecturing, organizing and lying as unrestingly as a politician, in chase of the Knighthood due not to him (he always called on his Maker to forbid such a thought) but as tribute to Chaucer. Yet, sometimes, he could break from his obsession and prove how a man's work will try to save the soul of him. He would tell us charmingly of copyists of the fifteenth century in England and the Low Countries, who had multiplied the Chaucer MSS., of which there remained — he gave us the exact number — and how each scribe could by him (and, he implied, by him alone) be distinguished from every other by some peculiarity of letter-formation, spacing or like trick of pen-work; and how he could fix the dates of their work within five years. Sometimes he would give us an hour of really interesting stuff and then return to his overdue ''recognition.'' The changes sickened me, but Manallace defended him, as a master in his own line who had revealed Chaucer to at least one grateful soul.

This, as far as I remembered, was the autumn when Manallace holidayed in the Shetlands or the Faroes, and came back with a stone ''quern'' — a hand corn-grinder. He said it interested him from the ethnological standpoint. His whim lasted till next harvest, and was followed by a religious spasm which, naturally, translated itself into literature. He showed me a battered and mutilated Vulgate of 1485, patched up the back with bits of legal parchments, which he had bought for thirty-five shillings. Some monk's attempt to rubricate chapter-initials had caught, it seemed, his forlorn fancy, and he dabbled in shells of gold and silver paint for weeks.

That also faded out, and he went to the Continent to get local colour for a love story, about Alva and the Dutch, and the next year I saw practically nothing of him. This released me from seeing much of Castorley, but, at intervals, I would go there to dine with him, when his wife — an unappetizing, ash-coloured woman — made no secret that his friends wearied her almost as much as he did. But a later meeting, not long after Manallace had finished his Low Countries' novel, I found Castorley charged to bursting-point with triumph and high information hardly withheld. He confided to me that a time was at hand when great matters would be made plain, and "recognition" would be inevitable. I assumed, naturally, that there was fresh scandal or heresy afoot in Chaucer circles, and kept my curiosity within bounds.

In time, New York cabled that a fragment of a hitherto unknown Canterbury Tale lay safe in the steel-walled vaults of the seven-million-dollar Sunnapia Collection. It was news on an international scale — the New World exultant — the Old deploring the "burden of British taxation which drove such treasures, etc.," and the lighter-minded journals disporting themselves according to their publics; for "our Dan," as one earnest Sunday editor observed, "lies closer to the national heart than we wot of." Common decency made me call on Castorley, who, to my surprise, had not yet descended into the arena. I found him, made young again by joy, deep in just-passed proofs.

Yes, he said, it was all true. He had, of course, been in it from the first. There had been found one hundred and seven new lines of Chaucer tacked on to an abridged end of *The Persone's Tale*, the whole the work of Abraham Mentzius, better known as Mentzel of Antwerp (1388-1438/9) — I might remember he had talked about him — whose distinguishing peculiarities were a certain Byzantine formation of his *g*'s, the use of a "sickle-slanted" reed pen, which cut into the vellum at certain letters; and, above all, a tendency to spell English words on Dutch lines, whereof the manuscript carried one convincing proof. For instance (he wrote it out for me), a girl praying against an undesired marriage, says:

"Ah Jesu-Moder, pitie my oe peyne.
Daiespringe mishandeelt cometh nat agayne."

Would I, please, note the spelling of "mishandeelt"? Stark Dutch and Mentzel's besetting sin! But in *his* position one took nothing for granted. The page had been part of the stiffening of the side of an old Bible, bought in a parcel by Dredd, the big dealer, because it had some rubricated chapter-initials, and by Dredd shipped, with a consignment of similar odds and ends, to the Sunnapia Collection, where they were making a glass-cased exhibit of the whole history of illumination and did not care how many books they gutted for that purpose. There, someone who noticed a crack in the back of the volume had unearthed it. He went on: "They didn't know what to make of the thing at first. But they knew about *me*! They kept quiet till I'd been consulted. You might have noticed I was out of England for three months.

"I was over there, of course. It was what is called a 'spoil' — a page Mentzel had spoiled with his Dutch spelling — I expect he had had the English dictated to him — then had evidently used the vellum for trying out his reeds; and then, I suppose, had put it away. The 'spoil' had been doubled, pasted together, and slipped in as stiffening to the old book-cover. I had it steamed open, and analysed the wash. It gave the flour grains in the paste — coarse, because of the old millstone — and there were traces of the grit itself. What? Oh, possibly a handmill of Mentzel's own time. He may have doubled the spoilt page and used it for part of a pad to steady woodcuts on. It may have knocked about his workshop for years. That, indeed, is practically certain because a beginner from the Low Countries has tried his reed on a few lines of some monkish hymn — not a bad lilt tho' — which must have been common form. Oh yes, the page may have been used in other books before it was used for the Vulgate. That doesn't matter, but *this* does. Listen! I took a wash, for analysis, from a blot in one corner — that would be after Mentzel had given up trying to make a possible page of it, and had grown careless — and I got the actual *ink* of the period! It's a practically eternal stuff compounded on — I've forgotten his name for the minute — the scribe at Bury St Edmunds, of course — hawthorn bark and wine. Anyhow, on *his* formula. *That* wouldn't interest you either, but, taken with all the other testimony, it clinches the thing. (You'll see it all in my Statement to the Press on Monday.) Overwhelming, isn't it?''

''Overwhelming,'' I said, with sincerity. ''Tell me what the tale was about, though. That's more in my line.''

''I know it; but *I* have to be equipped on all sides. The verses are relatively easy for one to pronounce on. The freshness, the fun, the humanity, the fragrance of it all, cries — no, shouts — itself as Dan's work. Why Daiespringe mishandled alone stamps it from Dan's mint. Plangent as doom, my dear boy — plangent as doom! It's all in my Statement. Well, substantially, the fragment deals with a girl whose parents wish her to marry an elderly suitor. The mother isn't so keen on it, but the father, an old Knight, is. The girl, of course, is in love with a younger and a poorer man. Common form? Granted. Then the father, who doesn't in the least want to, is ordered off to a Crusade and, by way of passing on the kick, as we used to say during the War, orders the girl to be kept in duress till his return or her consent to the old suitor. Common form, again? Quite so. That's too much for her mother. She reminds the old Knight of his age and infirmities, and the discomforts of Crusading. Are you sure I'm not boring you?''

''Not at all,'' I said, though time had begun to whirl backward through my brain to a red velvet, pomatum-scented, side room at Neminaka's and Manallace's set face intoning to the gas.

''You'll read it all in my Statement next week. The sum is that the old lady tells him of a certain Knight-adventurer on the French coast, who, for a consideration, waylays Knights who don't relish crusading and holds them to impossible ransoms till the trooping-season is over or they are returned sick.

He keeps a ship in the Channel to pick 'em up and transfers his birds to his castle ashore, where he has a reputation for doing 'em well. As the old lady points out:

'And if perchance thou fall into his honde
By God how canstow ride to Holilonde?'

"You see? Modern in essence as Gilbert and Sullivan, but handled as only Dan could! And she reminds him that 'Honour and olde bones' parted company long ago. He makes one splendid appeal for the spirit of chivalry:

'Lat all men change as Fortune may send,
But Knighthood beareth service to the end,'

and *then*, of course, he gives in:

'For what his woman willeth to be don
Her manne must or wauken Hell anon.'

"Then she hints that the daughter's young lover, who is in the Bordeaux wine trade, could open negotiations for a kidnapping without compromising him. And *then* that careless brute Mentzel spoils his page and chucks it! But there's enough to show what's going to happen. You'll see it all in my Statement. Was there ever anything in literary finds to hold a candle to it? . . . And they give grocers Knighthoods for selling cheese!"

I went away before he could get into his stride on that course. I wanted to think, and to see Manallace. But I waited till Castorley's Statement came out. He had left himself no loophole. And when, a little later, his (nominally the Sunnapia people's) "scientific" account of their analyses and tests appeared, criticism ceased, and some journals began to demand "public recognition." Manallace wrote me on this subject, and I went down to his cottage, where he at once asked me to sign a Memorial on Castorley's behalf. With luck, he said, we might get him a K.B.E. in the next Honours

List. Had I read the Statement?

"I have," I replied. "But I want to ask you something first. Do you remember the night you got drunk at Neminaka's, and I stayed behind to look after you?"

"Oh, *that* time," said he, pondering. "Wait a minute! I remember Graydon advancing me two quid. He was a generous paymaster. And I remember — now, who the devil rolled me under the sofa — and what for?"

"We all did," I replied. "You wanted to read us what you'd written to those Chaucer cuts."

"I don't remember that. No! I don't remember anything after the sofa episode. . . . *You* always said that you took me home — didn't you?"

"I did, and you told Kentucky Kate outside the old Empire that you had been faithful, Cynara, in your fashion."

"Did I?" said he. "My God! Well, I suppose I have." He stared into the fire. "What else?"

"Before we left Neminaka's you recited me what you had made out of the cuts — the whole tale! So — you see?"

"Ye-es." He nodded. "What are you going to do about it?"

"What are *you*?"

"I'm going to help him get his Knighthood — first."

"Why?"

"I'll tell you what he said about 'Dal's mother — the night there was that air-raid on the offices."

He told it.

"That's why," he said. "Am I justified?"

He seemed to me entirely so.

"But after he gets his Knighthood?" I went on.

"That depends. There are several things I can think of. It interests me."

"Good Heavens! I've always imagined you a man without interests."

"So I was. I owe my interests to Castorley. He gave me every one of 'em except the tale itself."

"How did *that* come?"

"Something in those ghastly cuts touched off something in

me — a sort of possession, I suppose. I was in love too. No wonder I got drunk that night. I'd *been* Chaucer for a week! Then I thought the notion might make a comic opera. But Gilbert and Sullivan were too strong."

"So I remember you told me at the time."

"I kept it by me, and it made me interested in Chaucer — philologically and so on. I worked on it on those lines for years. There wasn't a flaw in the wording even in '14. I hardly had to touch it after that."

"Did you ever tell it to anyone except me.?"

"No, only 'Dal's mother — when she could listen to anything — to put her to sleep. But when Castorley said — what he did about her, I thought I might use it. 'Twasn't difficult. *He* taught me. D'you remember my birdlime experiments, and the stuff on our hands? I'd been trying to get that ink for more than a year. Castorley told me where I'd find the formula. And your falling over the quern, too?"

"That accounted for the stone dust under the microscope?"

"Yes. I grew the wheat in the garden here, and ground it myself. Castorley gave me Mentzel complete. He put me on to an MS. in the British Museum which he said was the finest sample of his work. I copied his 'Byzantine *g*'s' for months."

"And what's a sickle-slanted pen?" I asked.

"You nick one edge of your reed till it drags and scratches on the curves of the letters. Castorley told me about Mentzel's spacing and margining. I only had to get the hang of his script."

"How long did that take you?"

"On and off — some years. I was too ambitious at first — I wanted to give the whole poem. That would have been risky. Then Castorley told me about spoiled pages and I took the hint. I spelt 'Dayspring mishandeelt' Mentzel's way — to make sure of him. It's not a bad couplet in itself. Did you see how he admires the 'plangency' of it?"

"Never mind him. Go on!" I said.

He did. Castorley had been his unfailing guide throughout, specifying in minutest detail every trap to be set later for his own feet. The actual vellum was an Antwerp find, and its introduction into the cover of the Vulgate was begun after a long course of amateur bookbinding. At last, he bedded it under pieces of an old deed, and a printed page (1686) of Horace's *Odes*, legitimately used for repairs by different owners in the seventeenth and eighteenth centuries; and at the last moment, to meet Castorley's theory that spoiled pages were used in workshops by beginners, he had written a few Latin words in fifteenth century script — the Statement gave the exact date — across an open part of the fragment. The thing ran: "*Illa alma Mater ecca, secum afferens me acceptum. Nicolaus Atrib.*" The disposal of the thing was easiest of all. He had merely hung about Dredd's dark bookshop of fifteen rooms, where he was well known, occasionally buying but generally browsing, till one day, Dredd Senior showed him a case of cheap black-letter stuff, English and Continental — being packed for the Sunnapia people — into which Manallace tucked his contribution, taking care to wrench the back enough to give a lead to an earnest seeker.

"And then?" I demanded.

"After six months or so Castorley sent for me. Sunnapia had found it, and as Dredd had missed it, and there was no money-motive sticking out, they were half convinced it was genuine from the start. But they invited him over. He conferred with their experts, and suggested the scientific tests. *I* put that into his head, before he sailed. That's all. And now, will you sign our Memorial?"

I signed. Before we had finished hawking it round there was a host of influential names to help us, as well as the impetus of all the literary discussion which arose over every detail of the glorious trove. The upshot was a K.B.E.* for Castorley in the next Honours List; and Lady Castorley, her cards duly printed, called on friends that same afternoon.

* Officially it was on account of his good work in the Departmental of Co-ordinated Supervisals, but all true lovers of literature knew the real reason, and told the papers so.

Manallace invited me to come with him, a day or so later, to convey our pleasure and satisfaction to them both. We were rewarded by the sight of a man relaxed and ungirt — not to say wallowing naked — on the crest of Success. He assured us that "The Title" should not make any difference to our future relations, seeing it was in no sense personal, but, as he had often said, a tribute to Chaucer; "and, after all," he pointed out, with a glance at the mirror over the mantelpiece, "Chaucer was the prototype of the 'veray parfit gentil Knight' of the British Empire so far as that then existed."

On the way back, Manallace told me he was considering either an unheralded revelation in the baser Press which should bring Castorley's reputation about his own ears some breakfast-time, or a private conversation, when he would make clear to Castorley that he must now back the forgery as long as he lived, under threat of Manallace's betraying it if he flinched.

He favoured the second plan. "If I pull the string of the shower-bath in the papers," he said, "Castorley might go off his veray parfit gentil nut. I want to keep his intellect."

"What about your own position? The forgery doesn't matter so much. But if you tell this you'll kill him," I said.

"I intend that. Oh — my position? I've been dead since — April, Fourteen, it was. But there's no hurry. What was it *she* was saying to you just as we left?"

"She told me how much your sympathy and understanding had meant to him. She said she thought that even Sir Alured did not realize the full extent of his obligations to you."

"She's right, but I don't like her putting it that way."

"It's only common form — as Castorley's always saying."

"Not with *her*. She can hear a man think."

"She never struck me in that light."

"*You* aren't playing against her."

"Guilty conscience, Manallace?"

"H'm! I wonder. Mine or hers? I *wish* she hadn't said that. More even than *he* realizes it. I won't call again for a while."

He kept away till we read that Sir Alured, owing to slight

indisposition, had been unable to attend a dinner given in his honour.

Inquiries brought word that it was but natural reaction, after strain, which, for the moment, took the form of nervous dyspepsia, and he would be glad to see Manallace at any time. Manallace reported him as rather pulled and drawn, but full of his new life and position, and proud that his efforts should have martyred him so much. He was going to collect, collate, and expand all his pronouncements and inferences into one authoritative volume.

"I must make an effort of my own," said Manallace. "I've collected nearly all his stuff about the Find that has appeared in the papers, and he's promised me everything that's missing. I'm going to help him. It will be a new interest."

"How will you treat it?" I asked.

"I expect I shall quote his deductions on the evidence, and parallel 'em with my experiments — the ink and the paste and the rest of it. It ought to be rather interesting."

"But even then there will only be your word. It's hard to catch up with an established lie," I said. "Especially when you've started it yourself."

He laughed. "I've arranged for *that* — in case anything happens to me. Do you remember the 'Monkish Hymn'?"

"Oh yes! There's quite a literature about it already."

"Well, you write those ten words above each other, and read down the first and second letters of 'em; and see what you get.* My Bank has the formula."

He wrapped himself lovingly and leisurely round his new

* *Illa*
alma
Mater
ecca
secum
afferens
me
acceptum
Nicolaus
Atrib.

task, and Castorley was as good as his word in giving him help. The two practically collaborated, for Manallace suggested that all Castorley's strictly scientific evidence should be in one place, with his deductions and dithyrambs as appendices. He assured him that the public would prefer this arrangement, and, after grave consideration, Castorley agreed.

"That's better," said Manallace to me. "Now I sha'n't have so many hiatuses in my extracts. Dots always give the reader the idea you aren't dealing fairly with your man. I shall merely quote him solid, and rip him up, proof for proof, and date for date, in parallel columns. His book's taking more out of him than I like, though. He's been doubled up twice with tummy attacks since I've worked with him. And he's just the sort of flatulent beast who may go down with appendicitis."

We learned before long that the attacks were due to gallstones, which would necessitate an operation. Castorley bore the blow very well. He had full confidence in his surgeon, an old friend of theirs; great faith in his own constitution; a strong conviction that nothing would happen to him till the book was finished, and, above all, the Will to Live.

He dwelt on these assets with a voice at times a little out of pitch and eyes brighter than usual beside a slightly sharpening nose.

I had only met Gleeag, the surgeon, once or twice at Castorley's house, but had always heard him spoken of as a most capable man. He told Castorley that his trouble was the price exacted, in some shape or other, from all who had served their country; and that, measured in units of strain, Castorley had practically been at the front through those three years he had served in the Office of Co-ordinated Supervisals. However, the thing had been taken betimes, and in a few weeks he would worry no more about it.

"But suppose he dies?" I suggested to Manallace.

"He won't. I've been talking to Gleeag. He says he's all right."

"Wouldn't Gleeag's talk be common form?"

"I *wish* you hadn't said that. But, surely, Gleeag wouldn't have the face to play with me — or her."

"Why not? I expect it's been done before."

But Manallace insisted that, in this case, it would be impossible.

The operation was a success and, some weeks later, Castorley began to recast the arrangement and most of the material of his book. "Let me have my way," he said, when Manallace protested. "They are making too much of a baby of me. I really don't need Gleeag looking in every day now." But Lady Castorley told us that he required careful watching. His heart had felt the strain, and fret or disappointment of any kind must be avoided. "Even," she turned to Manallace, "though you know ever so much better how his book should be arranged than he does himself."

"But really," Manallace began. "I'm very careful not to fuss —"

She shook her finger at him playfully. "You don't think you do; but, remember, he tells me everything that you tell him, just the same as he told me everything that he used to tell *you*. Oh, I don't mean the things that men talk about. I mean about his Chaucer."

"I didn't realize that," said Manallace, weakly.

"I thought you didn't. He never spares me anything; but *I* don't mind," she replied with a laugh, and went off to Gleeag, who was paying his daily visit. Gleeag said he had no objection to Manallace working with Castorley on the book for a given time — say twice a week — but supported Lady Castorley's demand that he should not be over-taxed in what she called "the sacred hours." The man grew more and more difficult to work with, and the little check he had heretofore set on his self-praise went altogether.

"He says there has never been anything in the History of Letters to compare with it," Manallace groaned. "He wants now to inscribe — he never dedicates, you know — inscribe it to me, as his most valued assistant. The devil of it is that *she* backs him up in getting it out soon. Why? How much do you think she knows?"

"Why should she know anything at all?"

"You heard her say he had told her everything that he had told me about Chaucer? (I *wish* she hadn't said that!) If she puts two and two together, she can't help seeing that every one of his notions and theories has been played up to. But then — but then . . . Why is she trying to hurry publication? She talks about me fretting him. *She's* at him, all the time, to be quick."

Castorley must have over-worked, for, after a couple of months, he complained of a stitch in his right side, which Gleeag said was a slight sequel, a little incident of the operation. It threw him back awhile, but he returned to his work undefeated.

The book was due in the autumn. Summer was passing, and his publisher urgent, and — he said to me, when after a longish interval I called — Manallace had chosen this time, of all, to take a holiday. He was not pleased with Manallace, once his indefatigable *aide*, but now dilatory, and full of time-wasting objections. Lady Castorley had noticed it, too.

Meantime, with Lady Castorley's help, he himself was doing the best he could to expedite the book; but Manallace had mislaid (did I think through jealousy?) some essential stuff which had been dictated to him. And Lady Castorley wrote Manallace, who had been delayed by a slight motor accident abroad, that the fret of waiting was prejudicial to her husband's health. Manallace, on his return from the Continent, showed me that letter.

"He has fretted a little, I believe," I said.

Manallace shuddered. "If I stay abroad, I'm helping to kill him. If I help him to hurry up the book, I'm expected to kill him. *She* knows," he said.

"You're mad. You've got this thing on the brain."

"I have not! Look here! You remember that Gleeag gave me from four to six, twice a week, to work with him. She called them the 'sacred hours'. You heard her? Well, they *are*! They are Gleeag's and hers. But she's so infernally plain, and I'm such a fool, it took me weeks to find it out."

"That's their affair," I answered. "It doesn't prove she knows anything about the Chaucer."

"She *does*! He told her everything that he had told me when I was pumping him, all those years. She put two and two together when the thing came out. She saw exactly how I had set my traps. I know it! She's been trying to make me admit it."

"What did you do?"

"Didn't understand what she was driving at, of course. And then she asked Gleeag, before me, if he didn't think the delay over the book was fretting Sir Alured. He didn't think so. He said getting it out might deprive him of an interest. He had that much decency. *She's* the devil!"

"What do you suppose is her game, then?"

"If Castorley knows he's been had, it'll kill him. She's at me all the time, indirectly, to let it out. I've told you she wants to make it a sort of joke between us. Gleeag's willing to wait. He knows Castorley's a dead man. It slips out when they talk. They say 'He was,' not 'He is.' Both of 'em know it. But *she* wants him finished sooner."

"I don't believe it. What are you going to do?"

"What *can* I? I'm not going to have him killed, though."

Manlike, he invented compromises whereby Castorley might be lured up by paths of interest, to delay publication. This was not a success. As autumn advanced Castorley fretted more, and suffered from returns of his distressing colics. At last, Gleeag told him that he thought they might be due to an overlooked gallstone working down. A second comparatively trivial operation would eliminate the bother once and for all. If Castorley cared for another opinion, Gleeag named a surgeon of eminence. "And then," said he, cheerily, "the two of us can talk you over." Castorley did not want to be talked over. He was oppressed by pains in his side, which, at first, had yielded to the liver tonics Gleeag prescribed; but now they stayed — like a toothache — behind everything. He felt most at ease in his bedroom-study, with his proofs round him. If he had more pain than he could stand, he would consider the second operation. Meantime Manallace — "the meticulous Manallace," he called him — agreed with him in thinking that the Mentzel page-facsimile, done by the Sunnapia Library, was not quite good enough for the great book, and the Sunnapia people were, very decently, having it reprocessed. This would hold things back till early spring, which had its advantages, for he could run a fresh eye over all in the interval.

One gathered these news in the course of stray visits as the days shortened. He insisted on Manallace keeping to the "sacred hours," and Manallace insisted on my accompanying him when possible. On these occasions he and Castorley would confer apart for half an hour or so, while I listened to an unendurable clock in the drawing room. Then I would join them and help wear out the rest of the time, while Castorley rambled. His speech, now, was often clouded and uncertain — the result of the "liver tonics"; and his face came to look like old vellum.

It was a few days after Christmas — the operation had been postponed till the following Friday — that we called together. She met us with word that Sir Alured had picked up an irritating little winter cough, due to a cold wave, but we were not, therefore, to abridge our visit. We found him in steam perfumed with Friar's Balsam. He waved the old Sunnapia facsimile at us. We agreed that it ought to have been more worthy. He took a dose of his mixture, lay back and asked us to lock the door. There was, he whispered, something wrong somewhere. He could not lay his finger on it, but it was in the air. He felt he was being played with. He did not like it. There was something wrong all round him. Had we noticed it? Manallace and I severally and slowly denied that we had noticed anything of the sort.

With no longer break than a light fit of coughing, he fell into the hideous, helpless panic of the sick — those worse than captives who lie at the judgement and mercy of the hale for every office and hope. He wanted to go away. Would we help him to pack his Gladstone? Or, if that would attract too much attention in certain quarters, help him to dress and go out? There was an urgent matter to be set right, and now that he had The Title and knew his own mind it would all end happily and he would be well again. *Please* would we let him go out, just to speak to — he named her; he named her by her "little" name out of the old Neminaka days? Manallace quite agreed, and recommended a pull at the "liver tonic" to brace him after so long in the house. He took it, and Manallace suggested that it would be better if, after his walk, he came down to the cottage for a week end and brought the revise with him. They could then retouch the last chapter. He answered to that drug and to some praise of his work, and presently simpered drowsily. Yes, it *was* good — though he said it who should not. He praised himself awhile till, with a puzzled forehead and shut eyes, he told us that *she* had been saying lately that it was too good — the whole thing, if we understood, was *too* good. He wished us to get the exact shade of her meaning. She had suggested, or rather implied, this doubt. She had said — he would let us draw our own inferences — that the Chaucer find had "anticipated the wants of humanity," Johnson, of course. No need to tell *him* that. But what the hell was her implication? Oh God! Life had always been one long innuendo! *And* she had said that a man could do anything with anyone if he saved him the trouble of thinking. What did she mean by that? *He* had never shirked thought. He had thought sustainedly all his life. It *wasn't* too good was it? Manallace didn't think it was too good — did he? But this pick-pick-picking at a man's brain and work was too bad, wasn't it? *What* did she mean? Why did she always bring in Manallace, who was only a friend — no scholar, but a lover of the game — Eh? — Manallace could confirm this if he were here, instead of loafing on the Continent just when he was most needed.

"I've come back," Manallace interrupted, unsteadily. "I can confirm every word you've said. You've nothing to worry about. It's *your* find — *your* credit — *your* glory and — all the rest of it."

"Swear you'll tell her so then," said Castorley. "She doesn't believe a word I say. She told me she never has since before we were married. Promise!"

Manallace promised, and Castorley added that he had named him his literary executor, the proceeds of the book to go to his wife. "All profits without deduction," he gasped. "Big sales if it's properly handled. *You* don't need money. . . . Graydon'll trust *you* to any extent. It'ud be a long . . ."

He coughed, and, as he caught breath, his pain broke through all the drugs, and the outcry filled the room. Manallace rose to fetch Gleeag, when a full, high, affected voice, unheard for a generation, accompanied, as it seemed, the clamour of a beast in agony, saying: "I wish to God someone would stop that old swine howling down there! *I* can't . . . I was going to tell you fellows that it would be a dam' long time before Graydon advanced *me* two quid . . ."

We escaped together, and found Gleeag waiting, with Lady Castorley, on the landing. He telephoned me, next morning, that Castorley had died of bronchitis, which his weak state made it impossible for him to throw off. "Perhaps it's just as well," he added, in reply to the condolences I asked him to convey to the widow. "We might have come across something we couldn't have coped with."

Distance from that house made me bold.

"You knew all along, I suppose? What was it, really?"

"Malignant kidney-trouble — generalized at the end. 'No use worrying him about it. We let him through as easily as possible. Yes! A happy release . . . What? . . . Oh! Cremation. Friday, at eleven."

There, then, Manallace and I met. He told me that she had asked him whether the book need now be published; and he had told her this was more than ever necessary, in her interests as well as Castorley's.

''She is going to be known as his widow — for a while, at any rate. Did I perjure myself much with him?''

''Not explicitly,'' I answered.

''Well, I have now — with *her* — explicitly,'' said he, and took out his black gloves . . .

As, on the appointed words, the coffin crawled sideways through the noiselessly-closing door-flaps, I saw Lady Castorley's eyes turn towards Gleeag.

Permission for Death Is Granted

Edmundo Valadés

Edmundo Valadés

(Mexico, b. 1915)

In 1810 Father Miguel Hidalgo y Costilla, a parish priest in the Mexican village of Dolores, tried to rouse the Indian peasants against their tyrannical Spanish masters and led them in the first outbreak of the Revolution which did not crystallize until almost a century later. In 1917, after a bloody civil war, a constitution was drawn up, granting ownership of lands and water to the Republic, which in turn had the right to bestow it to private persons. The terms of the constitution also excluded the Church from any involvement with public education, made marriage a civil contract and limited the activities of the clergy. The ruling aristocracy, however, paid little attention to the constitution.

The Mexican Revolution is one of the main themes of Mexican literature. Edmundo Valadés, for many years a leading journalist, chose to chronicle the peasants' struggles in his two books of short stories, *Permission for Death Is Granted* and *Sinister Dualities*. In the following story, — the first translation of Valadés's work in English — the author has not tried to parrot the Indians' voice or reproduce their dialect; instead he has succeeded in mirroring through their speech their quiet dignity, and a glimpse of the world which was taken away from them and then flung back, unusable.

Permission for Death Is Granted

On the platform the engineers are talking, laughing. They slap each other on the backs and tell clever jokes, a few dirty stories with hard punchlines. Little by little their attention is drawn towards the crowd in the hall. They stop discussing their latest party, giving the details about the new girl in the whorehouse. Their talk now turns to the men below, the collective farmers attending the assembly, down there, in front of them.

"Of course they must be saved. Assimilate them into our own civilization, cleanse their skin, corrupt their souls."

"You're sceptical, sir. And you doubt our efforts, and the efforts of the Mexican Revolution."

"You know it's useless. Those monkeys are hopeless. They're rotten with liquor, with ignorance. Look what came from giving them the land."

"You only see the obvious: you're a defeatist, my friend. We are the ones to blame. We gave them the land, and then? We sat back, terribly pleased with ourselves. But what about the mortgage payments, the fertilizers, the new techniques, the machinery? Will they invent all that on their own?"

The chairman, playing with his moustache, looks down at the hall through his glasses, unconcerned with the comings and goings of the engineers. When the strong, earthy animal smell of the men settling down on the benches reaches his nostrils, he takes out a coloured handkerchief and blows into it noisily. He also was once a peasant, but that was long ago. Now, thanks to the city and his official position, all that is left from those days are his handkerchief and the calluses on his hands.

The men in the hall take their seats solemnly, with the wariness peasants always show when entering a closed room, an assembly hall or a church. They say only a few words; they talk about harvests, rain, farm animals, mortgages. Many carry net lunchbags hanging from their shoulders, ready in case they get hungry. A few are smoking calmly, in no hurry, as if the cigarettes were growing out of their very hands. Others stand, leaning against the side walls, their arms crossed over their chests, mounting a peaceful guard.

The chairman shakes his bell and the sound makes the voices fade away. The engineers begin. They speak of technical problems, of the need of increasing production, of improving the crops. They promise to help the farmers, they urge them to voice their needs.

"We want to help, you can trust us."

Now it's the turn of the men in the hall. The chairman invites them to speak out. One hand rises slowly, timidly. Others follow. The farmers mention a few of their problems: the water, the elders, the mortgage, the school. Some are precise, to the point; others get entangled in their words, don't manage to make themselves clear. They scratch their heads and turn around to try and find what they were going to say, as if the idea had gone and hidden itself somewhere else, in the eyes of a fellow worker, or high above their heads where the lamp is hanging.

There, in one corner, a few of the men are whispering.

They are all from the same village. Something serious seems to be worrying them. They consult with one another, discussing who is to speak for all of them.

"I think it should be Jilipe. He knows a lot."

"You, Juan, you spoke the other time."

They can't make up their minds. The men whose names have been mentioned wait to be pushed forward. An old farmer, perhaps one of the elders, decides for them:

"Let it be Sacramento."

Sacramento waits.

"Go on, lift your hand."

The hand goes up but the chairman doesn't see it. Others are more visible and are called first. Sacramento looks at the old man. One of the younger farmers, almost a boy, lifts his hand as high as it will go. Over the forest of hairy heads five dark fingers appear, dirty with earth. The chairman sees the hand. The group has the floor.

"Now stand up."

The hand goes down as Sacramento rises to his feet. He tries to find a place for his hat. The hat becomes a vast nuisance, it grows, it doesn't seem to fit anywhere. Sacramento holds it in his hands. The men at the table become impatient. The chairman's voice springs up, full of authority, of command:

"You! You asked to speak. We're waiting."

Sacramento fixes his eyes on the engineer at the far end of the table. It seems as if he will speak only to him, as if the others had all disappeared and only the two of them had remained in the room.

"I want to speak for all of us at San Juan de las Manzanas. We bring a complaint against the municipal president because he's always fighting us and we can't take it no more. First he took some land away from Felipe Perez and Juan Hernandez because it was next to his own. We sent a telegram to Mexico City and they didn't even bother to answer. We got together and talked, and thought that it would be a good idea to go to the Agricultural Committee to get the lands back. Well, it was of no use, neither going there nor showing the papers. The municipal president kept the lands."

Sacramento speaks without changing the expression on his face, as if he were mumbling some kind of old prayer of which he knows both the beginning and the end by heart.

"So then, when he saw us all angry, he accused us of being troublemakers. You would have thought it was us who had taken the lands. And then he came back with his accounts — mortgage papers, sir. He said we were behind in the payments. And the agent agreed. He said we had to pay all sorts of interests. Crescencio, who lives over the hill, near the water, and who understands about numbers, added them up and saw that it wasn't true: he just wanted to make us pay more. So the municipal president brought some gentlemen from Mexico City, with all kinds of documents, and they said that if we didn't pay they'd take all our lands away. You see, so to speak, he made us pay for what we didn't owe him . . . ."

Sacramento tells his story with no emphasis, with no deliberate pauses. It's as if he were plowing the land. His words fall like seeds, sowing.

"Then afterwards the thing about my son, sir. The boy's hot-blooded, sir. I didn't want him to do it. I tried to stop him. He had drunk a bit and the wine had gone to his head. There was nothing I could do. He went out to find the municipal president, to talk to him, face to face . . . They killed the boy, just like that, saying that he was stealing one of the municipal president's cows. They sent him back dead, his face blown to shreds . . . ."

Sacramento's throat trembles. Only that. He's still standing, like a tree that has taken root. Nothing else. His eyes are still fixed on the engineer, the same one at the far end of the table.

"Then there was the water. Because there was very little, because of the bad rains, the Municipal President had closed the canal. And the cornfields were drying up, and the people were fearing a bad year . . . so we went to see him, to ask him to give us just a little water, sir, just enough for our crops. And he greeted us with angry words, and wouldn't listen. He didn't even get off his mule, to spite us.''

A hand tugs at Sacramento's sleeve. One of his fellow farmers whispers something to him. Sacramento's voice is the only sound in the hall.

''If this were not enough — because, thanks to the Holy Virgin, there were more rains and we saved about half the crops — there was what happened on Saturday. The Municipal President went out with his men, bad men they are, and stole two of our girls: Lupita, who was going to marry Herminio, and Crescencio's daughter. They took us all by surprise, because we were out in the fields, and so we couldn't stop them. They dragged them struggling to the hills and then left them there. When the girls managed to get back they were in very bad shape, beaten up and everything. We didn't have to ask to know what had happened. And now the people were really furious, fed up of having to be at the mercy of such a master.''

For the first time Sacramento's voice shook, with menace, anger, determination.

''And as no one will listen to us, because we've been to all the authorities and we don't know where justice is to be found, we want to make arrangements here. You,'' and Sacramento's eyes now swept the engineers until they reached the head of the table, ''you, who promised us help, we ask your permission to punish the municipal president of San Juan de laz Manzanas. We ask you to allow us to take justice in our hands . . . .''

All eyes are now fixed on the men on the platform. The chairman and the engineers look at each other in silence. Then they talk.

''This is absurd. We can't allow this unthinkable request.''

''No, my friend. It's not absurd. Absurd would be to leave the matter in the hands of those who have done nothing, of those who haven't even listened. It would be cowardly to wait until our justice made justice. These men would never believe in us again. I'd rather stand on these men's side, with their primitive justice, yes, but justice of some kind, and assume whatever responsibility is to be assumed. As far as I'm concerned we simply have to grant them what they ask."

"But we're civilized, we've got institutions; we can't just set them aside."

"It would be justifying outlaws, savages."

"What worse outlaw than the man they accuse? If he had offended us as he has offended them, if he had caused us the grievances he has caused them, we would certainly have killed him. We would certainly have ignored a system of justice that doesn't work. I say that we should vote on their proposal."

"I agree."

"But these people are all liars; we should at least try to find out the truth. And anyway, we have no authority to grant a request like that."

Now the chairman intervenes. The peasant inside him rises to speak. His voice admits no argument.

"The assembly will decide. I'll take the responsibility."

He turns towards the hall. His voice is a peasant's voice, the same voice that he must have used in the hills, mixed with the earth, speaking to his people.

"We are voting on the proposal of the farmers of San Juan de las Manzanas. Those who agree they should be given permission to execute the Municipal President, please raise your hands . . ."

All hands rise. Even those of the engineers. There is not a single man who has not lifted his hand, showing his approval. Each finger points to an immediate, unavoidable death.

"The assembly grants permission to the farmers of San Jaun de las Manzanas for their request."

Sacramento, who has remained standing, calmly finishes his speech. There is neither joy nor pain in what he is about to say. His expression is serene, clear-cut.

"Thank you for the permission, sir, because, as no one would listen to us, since yesterday morning the municipal president of San Juan de las Manzanas is dead."

Translated from the Spanish by Alberto Manguel

Torridge

William Trevor

William Trevor

(Ireland, b. 1928)

More than the novel, the short story seems intent on pinpointing a moment, framing a scene, dissecting a situation as it takes place, pulling the strings of the plot down to the very last consequence. James Joyce, in *Dubliners*, discovered that nothing actually needs to happen in a short story: the moment presented may in fact simply echo the past and mirror the future, drawing its effectiveness from the precarious teetering between what was and what will be. William Trevor explores a similar moment in "Torridge," which is certainly one of his most powerful short stories. Summing up Trevor's many novels and short-story collections, John Fowles pointed out that "art of this solidity and quality cannot be written from inside frontiers. It is, in the best sense of the word, international."

Torridge

Perhaps nobody ever did wonder what Torridge would be like as a man — or what Wiltshire or Mace-Hamilton or Arrowsmith would be like, come to that. Torridge at thirteen had a face with a pudding look, matching the sound of his name. He had small eyes and short hair like a mouse's. Within the collar of his grey regulation shirt the knot of his House tie was formed with care, a maroon triangle of just the right shape and bulk. His black shoes were always shiny.

Torridge was unique in some way: perhaps only because he was beyond the pale and appeared, irritatingly, to be unaware of it. He wasn't good at games and had difficulty in understanding what was being explained in the classroom. He would sit there frowning, half smiling, his head a little to one side. Occasionally he would ask some question that caused an outburst of groaning. His smile would increase then. He would glance around the classroom, not flustered or embarrassed in the least, seeming to be pleased that he had caused such a response. He was naïve to the point where it was hard to believe he wasn't pretending, but his naïveté was real and was in time universally recognised as such. A master called Buller Yeats reserved his cruellest shafts of scorn for it, sighing whenever his eyes chanced to fall on Torridge, pretending to believe his name was Porridge.

Of the same age as Torridge, but similar in no other way, were Wiltshire, Mace-Hamilton and Arrowsmith. All three of them were blond-haired and thin, with a common sharpness about their features. They wore, untidily, the same clothes as Torridge, their House ties knotted any old how, the laces in their scuffed shoes often tied in several places. They excelled at different games and were quick to sense what was what. Attractive boys, adults had more than once called them.

The friendship among the three of them developed because, in a way, Torridge was what he was. From the first time they were aware of him — on the first night of their first term — he appeared to be special. In the darkness after lights-out someone was trying not to sob and Torridge's voice was piping away, not homesick in the least. His father had a button business was what he was saying: he'd probably be going into the button business himself. In the morning he was identified, a boy in red and blue striped pyjamas, still chattering in the washroom. "What's your father do, Torridge?" Arrowsmith asked at breakfast, and that was the beginning. "Dad's in the button business," Torridge beamingly replied. "Torridge's, you know." But no one did know.

He didn't, as other new boys, make a particular friend. For a while he attached himself to a small gang of homesick boys who had only their malady in common, but after a time this gang broke up and Torridge found himself on his own, though it seemed quite happily so. He was often to be found in the room of the kindly housemaster of Junior House, an ageing white-haired figure called Old Frosty, who listened sympathetically to complaints of injustice at the hands of other masters, always ready to agree that the world was a hard place. "You should hear Buller Yeats on Torridge, sir," Wiltshire used to say in Torridge's presence. "You'd think Torridge had no feelings, sir." Old Frosty would reply that

Buller Yeats was a frightful man. "Take no notice, Torridge," he'd add in his kindly voice, and Torridge would smile, making it clear that he didn't mind in the least what Buller Yeats said. "Torridge knows true happiness," a new young master, known as Mad Wallace, said in an unguarded moment one day, a remark which caused immediate uproar in a Geography class. It was afterwards much repeated, like "Dad's in the button business" and "Torridge's, you know." The true happiness of Torridge became a joke, the particular property of Wiltshire and Mace-Hamilton and Arrowsmith. Furthering the joke, they claimed that knowing Torridge was a rare experience, that the private realm of his innocence and his happiness was even exotic. Wiltshire insisted that one day the school would be proud of him. The joke was worked to death.

At the school it was the habit of certain senior boys to "take an interest in" juniors. This varied from glances and smiles across the dining hall to written invitations to meet in some secluded spot at a stated time. Friendships, taking a variety of forms, were then initiated. It was flattering, and very often a temporary antidote for homesickness, when a new boy received the agreeable but bewildering attentions of an important fifth-former. A meeting behind Chapel led to the negotiating of a barbed-wire fence on a slope of gorse bushes, the older boy solicitous and knowledgeable. There were well-trodden paths and nooks among the gorse where smoking could take place with comparative safety. Farther afield, in the hills, there were crude shelters composed of stones and corrugated iron. Here, too, the emphasis was on smoking and romance.

New boys very soon became aware of the nature of older boys' interest in them. The flattery changed its shape, an adjustment was made — or the new boys retreated in panic from this area of school life. Andrews and Butler, Webb and Mace-Hamilton, Dillon and Pratt, Tothill and Goldfish Stewart, Good and Wiltshire, Sainsbury Major and Arrowsmith, Brewitt and King: the liaisons were renowned, the combinations of names sometimes seeming like a music hall turn, a soft-shoe shuffle of entangled hearts. There was faithlessness, too: the Honourable Anthony Swain made the rounds of the senior boys, a fickle and tartish *bijou*, desired and yet despised.

Torridge's puddingy appearance did not suggest that he had *bijou* qualities, and glances did not readily come his way in the dining-hall. This was often the fate, or good fortune, of new boys and was not regarded as a sign of qualities lacking. Yet quite regularly an ill-endowed child would mysteriously become the object of fifth- and sixth-form desire. This remained a puzzle to the juniors until they themselves became fifth- or sixth-formers and desire was seen to have to do with something deeper than superficial good looks.

It was the apparent evidence of this truth that caused Torridge, first of all, to be aware of the world of *bijou* and protector. He received a note from a boy in the Upper Fifth who had previously eschewed the sexual life offered by the school. He was a big, black-haired youth with glasses and a protruding forehead, called Fisher.

"Hey, what's this mean?" Torridge enquired, finding the note under his pillow, tucked into his pyjamas. "Here's a bloke wants to go for a walk."

He read the invitation out: "*If you would like to come for a walk meet me by the electricity plant behind Chapel. Half-past four Tuesday afternoon. R.A.J. Fisher.*"

"Jesus Christ!" said Armstrong.

"You've got an admirer, Porridge," Mace-Hamilton said.

"Admirer?"

"He wants you to be his *bijou*," Wiltshire explained.

"What's it mean, *bijou*?"

"Tart it means, Porridge."

"Tart?"

"Friend. He wants to be your protector."

"What's it mean, protector?"

"He loves you, Porridge."

"I don't even know the bloke."

"He's the one with the big forehead. He's a half-wit actually."

"Half-wit?"

"His mother let him drop on his head. Like yours did, Porridge."

"My mum never."

Everyone was crowding around Torridge's bed. The note was passed from hand to hand. "What's your dad do, Porridge?" Wiltshire suddenly asked, and Torridge automatically replied that he was in the button business.

"You've got to write a note back to Fisher, you know," Mace-Hamilton pointed out.

"Dear Fisher," Wiltshire prompted, "I love you."

"But I don't even —"

"It doesn't matter not knowing him. You've got to write a letter and put it in his pyjamas."

Torridge didn't say anything. He placed the note in the top pocket of his jacket and slowly began to undress. The other boys drifted back to their own beds, still amused by the development. In the washroom the next morning Torridge said:

"I think he's quite nice, that Fisher."

"Had a dream about him, did you, Porridge?" Mace-Hamilton enquired. "Got up to tricks, did he?"

"No harm in going for a walk."

"No harm at all, Porridge."

In fact, a mistake had been made. Fisher, in his haste or his excitement, had placed the note under the wrong pillow. It was Arrowsmith, still allied with Sainsbury Major, whom he wished to attract.

That this error had occurred was borne in on Torridge when he turned up at the electricity plant on the following Tuesday. He had not considered it necessary to reply to Fisher's note, but he had, across the dining-hall, essayed a smile or two in the older boy's direction: it had surprised him to meet with no response. It surprised him rather more to meet with no response by the electricity plant. Fisher just looked at him and then turned his back, pretending to whistle.

"Hullo, Fisher," Torridge said.

"Hop it, look. I'm waiting for someone."

"I'm Torridge, Fisher."

"I don't care who you are."

"You wrote me that letter." Torridge was still smiling. "About a walk, Fisher."

"Walk? What walk?"

"You put the letter under my pillow, Fisher."

"Jesus!" said Fisher.

The encounter was observed by Arrowsmith, Mace-Hamilton and Wiltshire, who had earlier taken up crouched positions behind one of the chapel buttresses. Torridge heard the familiar hoots of laughter, and because it was his way he joined in. Fisher, white-faced, strode away.

"Poor old Porridge," Arrowsmith commiserated, gasping and pretending to be contorted with mirth. Mace-Hamilton and Wiltshire were leaning against the buttress, issuing shrill noises.

"Gosh," Torridge said, "*I* don't care."

He went away, still laughing a bit, and there the matter of Fisher's attempt at communication might have ended. In fact it didn't, because Fisher wrote a second time and this time he made certain that the right boy received his missive. But Arrowsmith, still firmly the property of Sainsbury Major, wished to have nothing to do with R.A.J. Fisher.

When he was told the details of Fisher's error, Torridge said he'd guessed it had been something like that. But Wiltshire, Mace-Hamilton and Arrowsmith claimed that a new sadness had overcome Torridge. Something beautiful had been going to happen to him, Wiltshire said: just as the petals of friendship were opening the flower had been crudely snatched away. Arrowsmith said Torridge reminded him of one of Picasso's sorrowful harlequins. One way or the other, it was agreed that the experience would be beneficial to Torridge's sensitivity. It was seen as his reason for turning to religion, which recently he had done, joining a band of similarly inclined boys who were inspired by the word of the chaplain, a figure known as God Harvey. God Harvey was ascetic, seeming dangerously thin, his face all edge and as pale as paper, his cassock odorous with incense. He conducted readings in his room, offering coffee and biscuits afterwards, though not himself partaking of these refreshments. "God Harvey's linnets" his acolytes were called, for often a hymn was sung to round things off. Welcomed into this fold, Torridge regained his happiness.

R.A.J. Fisher, on the other hand, sank into greater gloom. Arrowsmith remained elusive, mockingly faithful to Sainsbury Major, haughty when Fisher glanced pleadingly, ignoring all his letters. Fisher developed a look of introspective misery. The notes that Arrowsmith delightedly showed around were full of longing, increasingly tinged with desperation. The following term, unexpectedly, Fisher did not return to the school.

There was a famous Assembly at the beginning of that term, with much speculation beforehand as to the trouble in the air. Rumour had it that once and for all an attempt was to be made to stamp out the smiles and the glances in the dining-hall, the whole business of *bijoux* and protectors, even the faithless behaviour of the Honourable Anthony Swain. The school waited and then the gowned staff arrived in the Assembly Hall and waited also, in grim anticipation on a raised dais. Public beatings for past offenders were scheduled, it was whispered: the Sergeant-major — the school's boxing instructor, who had himself told tales of public beatings in the past — would inflict the punishment at the headmaster's bidding. But that did not happen. Small and bald and red-skinned, the headmaster marched to the dais unaccompanied by the Sergeant-major. Twitching with anger that many afterwards declared had been simulated, he spoke at great length of the school's traditions. He stated that for fourteen years he had been proud to be its headmaster. He spoke of decency, and then of his own dismay. The school had been dishonoured; he would wish certain practices to cease. "I stand before you ashamed,'' he added, and paused for a moment. ''Let all this cease,'' he commanded. He marched away, tugging at his gown in a familiar manner.

No one understood why the Assembly had taken place at that particular time, on the first day of a summer term. Only the masters looked knowing, as though labouring beneath some secret, but pressed and pleaded with they refused to reveal anything. Even Old Frosty, usually a most reliable source on such occasions, remained awesomely tight-lipped.

But the pronounced dismay and shame of the headmaster changed nothing. That term progressed and the world of *bijoux* and their protectors continued as before, the glances, the meetings, cigarettes and romance in the hillside huts. R.A.J. Fisher was soon forgotten, having never made much of a mark. But the story of his error in placing a note under Torridge's pillow passed into legend, as did the encounter by the electricity plant and Torridge's deprivation of a relationship. The story was repeated as further terms passed by; new boys heard it and viewed Torridge with greater interest, imagining what R.A.J. Fisher had been like. The liaisons of Wiltshire with Good, Mace-Hamilton with Webb, and Arrowsmith with Sainsbury Major continued until the three senior boys left the school. Wiltshire, Mace-Hamilton and Arrowsmith found fresh protectors then, and later these new liaisons came to an end in a similar manner. Later still, Wiltshire, Mace-Hamilton and Arrowsmith ceased to be *bijoux* and became protectors themselves.

Torridge pursued the religious side of things. He continued to be a frequent partaker of God Harvey's biscuits and spiritual uplift, and a useful presence among the chapel pews, where he voluntarily dusted, cleaned brass, and kept the hymn-books in a state of repair with Sellotape. Wiltshire, Mace-Hamilton and Arrowsmith continued to circulate stories about him which were not true: that he was the product of virgin birth, that he possessed the gift of tongues but did not care to employ it, that he had three kidneys. In the end there emanated from them the claim that a liaison existed between

Torridge and God Harvey. "Love and the holy spirit," Wiltshire pronounced, suggesting an ambience of chapel fustiness and God Harvey's grey boniness. The swish of his cassock took on a new significance, as did his thin, dry fingers. In a holy way the fingers pressed themselves on to Torridge, and then their holiness became a passion that could not be imagined. It was all a joke because Torridge was Torridge, but the laughter it caused wasn't malicious because no one hated him. He was a figure of fun; no one sought his downfall because there was no downfall to seek.

The friendship between Wiltshire, Mace-Hamilton and Arrowsmith continued after they left the school, after all three had married and had families. Once a year they received the Old Boys' magazine, which told of the achievements of themselves and the more successful of their school-fellows. There were Old Boys' cocktail parties and Old Boys' Day at the school every June and the Old Boys' cricket match. Some of these occasions, from time to time, they attended. Every so often they received the latest rebuilding programme, with the suggestion that they might like to contribute to the rebuilding fund. Occasionally they did.

As middle age closed in, the three friends met less often. Arrowsmith was an executive with Shell and stationed for longish periods in different countries abroad. Once every two years he brought his family back to England, which provided an opportunity for the three friends to meet. The wives met on these occasions also, and over the years the children. Often the men's distant schooldays were referred to, Buller Yeats and Old Frosty and the Sergeant-major, the little red-skinned headmaster, and above all Torridge. Within the three families, in fact, Torridge had become a myth. The joke that had begun when they were all new boys together continued, as if driven by its own impetus. In the minds of the wives and children the innocence of Torridge, his true happiness in the face of mockery and his fondness for the religious side of life, all lived on. With some exactitude a physical image of the boy he'd been took root; his neatly knotted maroon House tie, his polished shoes, the hair that resembled a mouse's fur, the pudding face with two small eyes in it. "My dad's in the button business," Arrowsmith had only to say to cause instant laughter. "Torridge's, you know." The way Torridge ate, the way he ran, the way he smiled back at Buller Yeats, the rumour that he'd been dropped on his head as a baby, that he had three kidneys, all this was considerably appreciated, because Wiltshire and Mace-Hamilton and Arrowsmith related it well.

What was not related was R.A.J. Fisher's error in placing a note beneath Torridge's pillow, or the story that had laughingly been spread about concerning Torridge's relationship with God Harvey. This would have meant revelations that weren't seemly in family circles, the explanation of the world of *bijou* and protector, the romance and cigarettes in the hillside huts, the entangling of hearts. The subject had been touched upon among the three husbands and their wives in the normal course of private conversation, although not everything had been quite recalled. Listening, the wives had formed the impression that the relationships between older and younger boys at their husbands' school were similar to the platonic admiration a junior girl had so often harboured for a senior girl at their own schools. And so the subject had been left.

One evening in June, 1976, Wiltshire and Mace-Hamilton met in a bar called the Vine, in Piccadilly Place. They hadn't seen one another since the summer of 1974, the last time Arrowsmith and his family had been in England. Tonight they were to meet the Arrowsmiths again, for a family dinner in the Woodlands Hotel, Richmond. On the last occasion the three families had celebrated their reunion at the Wiltshires' house in Cobham and the time before with the Mace-Hamiltons in Ealing. Arrowsmith insisted that it was a question of turn and turn about and every third time he arranged for the family dinner to be held at his expense at the Woodlands. It was convenient because, although the Arrowsmiths spent the greater part of each biennial leave with Mrs Arrowsmith's parents in Somerset, they always stayed for a week at the Woodlands in order to see a bit of London life.

In the Vine in Piccadilly Place Wiltshire and Mace-Hamilton hurried over their second drinks. As always, they were pleased to see one another, and both were excited at the prospect of seeing Arrowsmith and his family again. They still looked faintly alike. Both had balded and run to fat. They wore inconspicuous blue suits with a discreet chalk stripe, Wiltshire's a little smarter than Mace-Hamilton's.

"We'll be late," Wiltshire said, having just related how he'd made a small killing since the last time they'd met. Wiltshire operated in the import-export world; Mace-Hamilton was a chartered accountant.

They finished their drinks. "Cheerio," the barman called out to them as they slipped away. His voice was deferentially low, matching the softly-lit surroundings. "Cheerio, Gerry," Wiltshire said.

They drove in Wiltshire's car to Hammersmith, over the bridge and on to Barnes and Richmond. It was a Friday evening; the traffic was heavy.

"He had a bit of trouble, you know," Mace-Hamilton said.

"Arrows?"

"She took a shine to some guy in Mombasa."

Wiltshire nodded, poking the car between a cyclist and a taxi. He wasn't surprised. One night six years ago Arrowsmith's wife and he had committed adultery together at her suggestion. A messy business it had been, and afterwards he'd felt terrible.

In the Woodlands Hotel Arrowsmith, in a grey flannel suit, was not entirely sober. He, too, had run a bit of fat although, unlike Wiltshire and Mace-Hamilton, he hadn't lost any of his hair. Instead, it had dramatically changed colour: what Old Frosty had once called "Arrows' blond thatch" was grey now. Beneath it his face was pinker than it had been and he had taken to wearing spectacles, heavy and black-rimmed, making him look even more different from the boy he'd been.

In the bar of the Woodlands he drank whisky on his own, smiling occasionally to himself because tonight he had a surprise for everybody. After five weeks of being cooped up with his in-laws in Somerset he was feeling good. "Have one yourself, dear," he invited the barmaid, a girl with an excess of lipstick on a podgy mouth. He pushed his own glass towards her while she was saying she didn't mind if she did.

His wife and his three adolescent children, two boys and a girl, entered the bar with Mrs Mace-Hamilton. "Hi, hi, hi," Arrowsmith called out to them in a jocular manner, causing his wife and Mrs Mace-Hamilton to note that he was drunk again. They sat down while he quickly finished the whisky that had just been poured for him. "Put another in that for a start," he ordered the barmaid, and crossed the floor of the bar to find out what everyone else wanted.

Mrs Wiltshire and her twins, girls of twelve, arrived while drinks were being decided about. Arrowsmith kissed her, as he had kissed Mrs Mace-Hamilton. The barmaid, deciding that the accurate conveying of such a large order was going to be beyond him, came and stood by the two tables that the party now occupied. The order was given; an animated conversation began.

The three women were different in appearance and in manner. Mrs Arrowsmith was thin as a knife, fashionably dressed in a shade of ash-grey that reflected her ash-grey hair. She smoked perpetually, unable to abandon the habit. Mrs Wiltshire was small. Shyness caused her to coil herself up in the presence of other people so that she often resembled a ball. Tonight she was in pink, a faded shade. Mrs Mace-Hamilton was carelessly plump, a large woman attired in a carelessly chosen dress that had begonias on it. She rather frightened Mrs Wiltshire. Mrs Arrowsmith found her trying.

"Oh, heavenly little drink!" Mrs Arrowsmith said, briefly drooping her blue-tinged eyelids as she sipped her gin and tonic.

"It *is* good to see you," Mrs Mace-Hamilton gushed, beaming at everyone and vaguely raising her glass. "And how they've all grown!" Mrs Mace-Hamilton had not had children herself.

"Their boobs have grown, by God," the older Arrowsmith boy murmured to his brother, a reference to the Wiltshire twins. Neither of the two Arrowsmith boys went to their father's school: one was at a preparatory school in Oxford, the other at Charterhouse. Being of an age to do so, they both drank sherry and intended to drink as much of it as they possibly could. They found these family occasions tedious. Their sister, about to go to university, had determined neither to speak nor to smile for the entire evening. The Wiltshire twins were quite looking forward to the food.

Arrowsmith sat beside Mrs Wiltshire. He didn't say anything but after a moment he stretched a hand over her two knees and squeezed them in what he intended to be a brotherly way. He said without conviction that it was great to see her. He didn't look at her while he spoke. He didn't much care for hanging about with the women and children.

In turn Mrs Wiltshire didn't much care for his hand on her knees and was relieved when he drew it away. "Hi, hi, hi," he suddenly called out, causing her to jump. Wiltshire and Mace-Hamilton had appeared.

The physical similarity that had been so pronounced when the three men were boys and had been only faintly noticeable between Wiltshire and Mace-Hamilton in the Vine was clearly there again, as if the addition of Arrowsmith had supplied missing reflections. The men had thickened in the same way; the pinkness of Arrowsmith's countenance was a pinkness that tinged the other faces too. Only Arrowsmith's grey thatch of hair seemed out of place, all wrong beside the baldness of the other two: in their presence it might have been a wig, an impression it did not otherwise give. His grey flannel suit, beside their pinstripes, looked like something put on by mistake. "Hi, hi, hi," he shouted, thumping their shoulders.

Further rounds of drinks were bought and consumed. The

Arrowsmith boys declared to each other that they were drunk and made further *sotto voce* observations about the forming bodies of the Wiltshire twins. Mrs Wiltshire felt the occasion becoming easier as Cinzano Bianco coursed through her bloodstream. Mrs Arrowsmith was aware of a certain familiar edginess within her body, a desire to be elsewhere, alone with a man she did not know. Mrs Mace-Hamilton spoke loudly of her garden.

In time the party moved from the bar to the dining-room. "Bring us another round at the table," Arrowsmith commanded the lipsticked barmaid. "Quick as you can, dear."

In the large dim dining-room waiters settled them around a table with little vases of carnations on it, a long table beneath the chandelier in the centre of the room. Celery soup arrived at the table, and smoked salmon and pâté, and the extra rounds of drinks Arrowsmith had ordered, and bottles of Nuits St Georges, and bottles of Vouvray and Anjou Rosé, and sirloin of beef, chicken à la king and veal escalope. The Arrowsmith boys laughed shrilly, openly staring at the tops of the Wiltshire twins' bodies. Potatoes, peas, spinach and carrots were served. Mrs Arrowsmith waved the vegetables away and smoked between courses. It was after this dinner six years ago that she had made her suggestion to Wiltshire, both of them being the worse for wear and it seeming not to matter because of that. "Oh, *isn't* this jolly?" the voice of Mrs Mace-Hamilton boomed above the general hubbub.

Over Chantilly trifle and Orange Surprise the name of Torridge was heard. The name was always mentioned just about now, though sometimes sooner. "Poor old bean," Wiltshire said, and everybody laughed because it was the one subject they all shared. No one really wanted to hear about the Mace-Hamiltons' garden; the comments of the Arrowsmith boys were only for each other; Mrs Arrowsmith's needs could naturally not be voiced; the shyness of Mrs Wiltshire was private too. But Torridge was different. Torridge in a way was like an old friend now, existing in everyone's mind, a family subject. The Wiltshire twins were quite amused to hear of some freshly remembered evidence of Torridge's naïveté; for the Arrowsmith girl it was better at least than being questioned by Mrs Mace-Hamilton; for her brothers it was an excuse to bellow with simulated mirth. Mrs Mace-Hamilton considered that the boy sounded frightful, Mrs Arrowsmith couldn't have cared less. Only Mrs Wiltshire had doubts: she thought the three men were hard on the memory of the boy, but of course had not ever said so. To-night, after Wiltshire had recalled the time when Torridge had been convinced by Arrowsmith that Buller Yeats had dropped dead in his bath, the younger Arrowsmith boy told of a boy at his own school who'd been convinced that his sister's dog had died.

"Listen," Arrowsmith suddenly shouted out. "He's going to join us. Old Torridge."

There was laughter, no one believing that Torridge was going to arrive, Mrs Arrowsmith saying to herself that her husband was pitiful when he became as drunk as this.

"I thought it would be a gesture," Arrowsmith said. "Honestly. He's looking in for coffee."

"You bloody devil, Arrows," Wiltshire said, smacking the table with the palm of his hand.

"He's in the button business," Arrowsmith shouted. "Torridge's, you know."

As far as Wiltshire and Mace-Hamilton could remember, Torridge had never featured in an Old Boys' magazine. No news of his career had been printed, and certainly no obituary. It was typical, somehow, of Arrowsmith to have winkled him out. It was part and parcel of him to want to add another dimension to the joke, to recharge its batteries. For the sight of Torridge in middle age would surely make funnier the reported anecdotes.

"After all, what's wrong," demanded Arrowsmith noisily, "with old school pals all meeting up? The more the merrier."

He was a bully, Mrs Wiltshire thought: all three of them were bullies.

Torridge arrived at half-past nine. The hair that had been like a mouse's fur was still like that. It hadn't greyed any more;

the scalp hadn't balded. He hadn't run to fat; in middle age he'd thinned down a bit. There was even a lankiness about him now, which was reflected in his movements. At school he had moved slowly, as though with caution. Jauntily attired in a pale linen suit, he crossed the dining room of the Woodlands Hotel with a step as nimble as a tap dancer's.

No one recognized him. To the three men who'd been at school with him the man who approached their dinner table was a different person, quite unlike the figure that existed in the minds of the wives and children.

"My dear Arrows," he said, smiling at Arrowsmith. The smile was different too, a brittle snap of a smile that came and went in a matter-of-fact way. The eyes that had been small didn't seem so in his thinner face. They flashed with a gleam of some kind, matching the snap of his smile.

"Good God, it's never old Porridge!" Arrowsmith's voice was slurred. His face had acquired the beginnings of an alcoholic crimson, sweat glistened on his forehead.

"Yes, it's old Porridge," Torridge said quietly. He held his hand out towards Arrowsmith and then shook hands with Wiltshire and Mace-Hamilton. He was introduced to their wives, with whom he shook hands also. He was introduced to the children, which involved further hand-shaking. His hand was cool and rather bony: they felt it should have been damp.

"You're nicely in time for coffee, Mr Torridge," Mrs Mace-Hamilton said.

"Brandy more like," Arrowsmith suggested. "Brandy, old chap?"

"Well, that's awfully kind of you, Arrows. Chartreuse I'd prefer, really."

A waiter drew up a chair. Room was made for Torridge between Mrs Mace-Hamilton and the Arrowsmith boys. It was a frightful mistake, Wiltshire was thinking. It was mad of Arrowsmith.

Mace-Hamilton examined Torridge across the dinner table. The old Torridge would have said he'd rather not have anything alcoholic, that a cup of tea and a biscuit were more his line in the evenings. It was impossible to imagine this man saying his dad had a button business. There was a suavity about him that made Mace-Hamilton uneasy. Because of what had been related to his wife and the other wives and their children he felt he'd been caught out in a lie, yet in fact that wasn't the case.

The children stole glances at Torridge, trying to see him as the boy who'd been described to them, and failing to. Mrs Arrowsmith said to herself that all this stuff they'd been told over the years had clearly been rubbish. Mrs Mace-Hamilton was bewildered. Mrs Wiltshire was pleased.

"No one ever guessed," Torridge said, "what became of R.A.J. Fisher." He raised the subject suddenly, without introduction.

"Oh God, Fisher," Mace-Hamilton said.

"Who's Fisher?" the younger of the Arrowsmith boys enquired.

Torridge turned to flash his quick smile at the boy. "He left," he said. "In unfortunate circumstances."

"You've changed a lot, you know," Arrowsmith said. "Don't you think he's changed?" he asked Wiltshire and Mace-Hamilton.

"Out of recognition," Wiltshire said.

Torridge laughed easily. "I've become adventurous. I'm a late developer, I suppose."

"What kind of unfortunate circumstances?" the younger Arrowsmith boy asked. "Was Fisher expelled?"

"Oh no, not at all," Mace-Hamilton said hurriedly.

"Actually," Torridge said, "Fisher's trouble all began with the writing of a note. Don't you remember? He put it in my pyjamas. But it wasn't for me at all."

He smiled again. He turned to Mrs Wiltshire in a way that seemed polite, drawing her into the conversation. "I was an innocent at school. But innocence eventually slips away. I found my way about eventually."

"Yes, of course," she murmured. She didn't like him, even though she was glad he wasn't as he might have been.

There was malevolence in him, a ruthlessness that seemed like a work of art. He seemed like a work of art himself, as though in losing the innocence he spoke of he had recreated himself.

"I often wonder about Fisher," he remarked.

The Wiltshire twins giggled. "What's so great about this bloody Fisher?" the older Arrowsmith boy murmured, nudging his brother with an elbow.

"What're you doing these days?" Wiltshire asked, interrupting Mace-Hamilton, who had begun to say something.

"I make buttons," Torridge replied. "You may recall my father made buttons."

"Ah, here're the drinks," Arrowsmith rowdily observed.

"I don't much keep up with the school," Torridge said as the waiter placed a glass of Chartreuse in front of him. "I don't so much as think about it except for wondering about poor old Fisher. Our headmaster was a cretin,' he informed Mrs Wiltshire.

Again the Wiltshire twins giggled. The Arrowsmith girl yawned and her brothers giggled also, amused that the name of Fisher had come up again.

"You will have coffee, Mr Torridge?" Mrs Mace-Hamilton offered, for the waiter had brought a fresh pot to the table. She held it poised above a cup. Torridge smiled at her and nodded. She said:

"Pearl buttons d'you make?"

"No, not pearl."

"Remember those awful packet peas we used to have?" Arrowsmith enquired. Wiltshire said:

"Use plastics at all? In your buttons, Porridge?"

"No, we don't use plastics. Leathers, various leathers. And horn. We specialise."

"How very interesting!" Mrs Mace-Hamilton exclaimed.

"No, no. It's rather ordinary really." He paused, and then added, "Someone once told me that Fisher went into a timber business. But of course that was far from true."

"A chap was expelled a year ago," the younger Arrowsmith boy said, contributing this in order to cover up a fresh outburst of sniggering. "For stealing a transistor."

Torridge nodded, appearing to be interested. He asked the Arrowsmith boys where they were at school. The older one said Charterhouse and his brother gave the name of his preparatory school. Torridge nodded again and asked their sister and she said she was waiting to go to university. He had quite a chat with the Wiltshire twins about their school. They considered it pleasant the way he bothered, seeming genuinely to want to know. The giggling died away.

"I imagined Fisher wanted me for his *bijou*," he said when all that was over, still addressing the children. "Our place was riddled with fancy larks like that. Remember?" he added, turning to Mace-Hamilton.

"*Bijou*?" one of the twins asked before Mace-Hamilton could reply.

"A male tart," Torridge explained.

The Arrowsmith boys gaped at him, the older one with his mouth actually open. The Wiltshire twins began to giggle again. The Arrowsmith girl frowned, unable to hide her interest.

"The Honourable Anthony Swain," Torridge said, "was no better than a whore."

Mrs Arrowsmith, who for some minutes had been engaged with her own thoughts, was suddenly aware that the man who was in the button business was talking about sex. She gazed diagonally across the table at him, astonished that he should be talking in this way.

"Look here, Torridge," Wiltshire said, frowning at him and shaking his head. With an almost imperceptible motion he gestured towards the wives and children.

"Andrew and Butler. Dillon and Pratt. Tothill and Goldfish Stewart. Your dad," Torridge said to the Arrowsmith girls, "was always very keen. Sainsbury Major in particular."

"Now look here," Arrowsmith shouted, beginning to get to his feet and then changing his mind.

"My gosh, how they broke chaps' hearts, those three!"

"Please don't talk like this." It was Mrs Wiltshire who protested, to everyone's surprise, most of all her own. "The children are quite young, Mr Torridge."

Her voice had become a whisper. She could feel herself reddening with embarrassment, and a little twirl of sickness occurred in her stomach. Deferentially, as though appreciating the effort she had made, Torridge apologised.

"I think you'd better go," Arrowsmith said.

"You were right about God Harvey, Arrows. Gay as a grig he was, beneath that cassock. So was Old Frosty, as a matter of fact."

"Really!" Mrs Mace-Hamilton cried, her bewilderment turning into outrage. She glared at her husband, demanding with her eyes that instantly something should be done. But her husband and his two friends were briefly stunned by what Torridge had claimed for God Harvey. Their schooldays leapt back at them, possessing them for a vivid moment: the dormitory, the dining-hall, the glances and the invitations, the meetings behind Chapel. It was somehow in keeping with the school's hypocrisy that God Harvey had had inclinations himself, that a rumour begun as an outrageous joke should have contained the truth.

"As a matter of fact," Torridge went on, "I wouldn't be what I am if it hadn't been for God Harvey. I'm what they call queer," he explained to the children. "I perform sexual acts with men."

"For God's sake, Torridge," Arrowsmith shouted, on his feet, his face the colour of ripe strawberry, his watery eyes quivering with rage.

"It was nice of you to invite me tonight, Arrows. Our *alma mater* can't be too proud of chaps like me."

People spoke at once, Mrs Mace-Hamilton and Mrs Wiltshire, all three men. Mrs Arrowsmith sat still. What she was thinking was that she had become quietly drunk while her husband had more boisterously reached the same condition. She was thinking, as well, that by the sound of things he'd possessed as a boy a sexual urge that was a lot livelier than the one he'd once exposed her to and now hardly ever did. With boys who had grown to be men he had had a whale of a time. Old Frosty had been a kind of Mr Chips, she'd been told. She'd never heard of Sainsbury Major or God Harvey.

"It's quite disgusting," Mrs Mace-Hamilton's voice cried out above the other voices. She said the police should be called. It was scandalous to have to listen to unpleasant conversation like this. She began to say the children should leaving the dining room, but changed her mind because it appeared that Torridge himself was about to go. "You're a most horrible man," she cried.

Confusion gathered, like a fog around the table. Mrs Wiltshire, who knew that her husband had committed adultery with Mrs Arrowsmith, felt another bout of nerves in her stomach. "Because she was starved, that's why," her husband had almost violently confessed when she'd discovered. "I was putting her out of her misery." She had wept then and he had comforted her as best he could. She had not told him that he had never succeeded in arousing in her the desire to make love: she had always assumed that to be a failing in herself, but now for some reason she was not so sure. Nothing had been directly said that might have caused this doubt, but an instinct informed Mrs Wiltshire that the doubt should be there. The man beside her smiled his brittle, malevolent smile at her, as if in sympathy.

With his head bent over the table and his hands half hiding his face, the younger Arrowsmith boy examined his father by glancing through his fingers. There were men whom his parents warned him against, men who would sit beside you in buses or try to give you a lift in a car. This man who had come tonight, who had been such a joke up till now, was apparently one of these, not a joke at all. And the confusion was greater: at one time, it seemed, his father had been like that too.

The Arrowsmith girl considered her father also. Once she

had walked into a room in Lagos to find her mother in the arms of an African clerk. Ever since she had felt sorry for her father. There'd been an unpleasant scene at the time, she'd screamed at her mother and later in a fury had told her father what she'd seen. He'd nodded, wearily seeming not to be surprised, while her mother had miserably wept. She'd put her arms around her father, comforting him; she'd felt no mercy for her mother, no sympathy or understanding. The scene formed vividly in her mind as she sat at the dinner table: it appeared to be relevant in the confusion and yet not clearly so. Her parents' marriage was messy, messier than it had looked. Across the table her mother grimly smoked, focussing her eyes with difficulty. She smiled at her daughter, a soft, inebriated smile.

The older Arrowsmith boy was also aware of the confusion. Being at a school where the practice which had been spoken of was common enough, he could easily believe the facts that had been thrown about. Against his will, he was forced to imagine what he had never imagined before: his father and his friends as schoolboys, engaged in passion with other boys. He might have been cynical about this image but he could not. Instead it made him want to gasp. It knocked away the smile that had been on his face all evening.

The Wiltshire twins unhappily stared at the white tablecloth, here and there stained with wine or gravy. They, too, found they'd lost the urge to smile and instead shakily blinked back tears.

"Yes, perhaps I'd better go," Torridge said.

With impatience Mrs Mace-Hamilton looked at her husband, as if expecting him to hurry Torridge off or at least to say something. But Mace-Hamilton remained silent. Mrs Mace-Hamilton licked her lips, preparing to speak herself. She changed her mind.

"Fisher didn't go into a timber business," Torridge said, "because poor old Fisher was dead as a doornail. Which is why our cretin of a headmaster, Mrs Mace-Hamilton, had that Assembly."

''Assembly?'' she said. Her voice was weak, although she'd meant it to sound matter-of-fact and angry.

''There was an Assembly that no one understood. Poor old Fisher had strung himself up in a barn on his father's farm. I discovered that,'' Torridge said, turning to Arrowsmith, ''years later: from God Harvey actually. The poor chap left a note but the parents didn't care to pass it on. I mean it was for you, Arrows.''

Arrowsmith was still standing, hanging over the table. ''Note?'' he said. ''For me?''

''Another note. Why d'you think he did himself in, Arrows?''

Torridge smiled, at Arrowsmith and then around the table.

''None of that's true,'' Wiltshire said.

''As a matter of fact it is.''

He went, and nobody spoke at the dinner table. A body of a schoolboy hung from a beam in a barn, a note on the straw below his dangling feet. It hung in the confusion that had been caused, increasing the confusion. Two waiters hovered by a sideboard, one passing the time by arranging sauce bottles, the other folding napkins into cone shapes. Slowly Arrowsmith sat down again. The silence continued as the conversation of Torridge continued to haunt the dinner table. He haunted it himself, with his brittle smile and his tap dancer's elegance, still faithful to the past in which he had so signally failed, triumphant in his middle age.

Then Mrs Arrowsmith quite suddenly wept and the Wiltshire twins wept and Mrs Wiltshire comforted them. The Arrowsmith girl got up and walked away, and Mrs Mace-Hamilton turned to the three men and said they should be ashamed of themselves, allowing all this to happen.

Other Titles in This Series

The Day the [illegible]
[illegible]

Café le Dog
Matt Cohen

High Spirits
Robertson Davies

The Pool in the Desert
Sara Jeannette Duncan

The [illegible]
[illegible]

Dinner Along the Amazon
Timothy Findley

Fables of Brunswick Avenue
Katherine Govier

[illegible] Book of [illegible]
edited by Wayne Grady

[illegible]

The Moccasin Telegraph and Other Stories
W. P. Kinsella

The Thief of [illegible]
[illegible]

Champagne Barn
Norman Levine

Darkness
Bharati Mukherjee

The Street
Mordecai Richler

Melancholy Elephants
Spider Robinson

PENGUIN · SHORT · FICTION

Other Titles In This Series

The Day is Dark/Three Travellers
Marie-Claire Blais

Café le Dog
Matt Cohen

High Spirits
Robertson Davies

The Pool In the Desert
Sara Jeannette Duncan

The Tattooed Woman
Marian Engel

Dinner Along the Amazon
Timothy Findley

Fables of Brunswick Avenue
Katherine Govier

Penguin Book of Canadian Short Stories
edited by Wayne Grady

Treasure Island
Jean Howarth

The Moccasin Telegraph and Other Stories
W.P. Kinsella

The Thrill of the Grass
W.P. Kinsella

Champagne Barn
Norman Levine

Darkness
Bharati Mukherjee

The Street
Mordecai Richler

Melancholy Elephants
Spider Robinson